M343

Applications of probability

BOOK 2

Modelling events in time and space

About M343

M343 *Applications of probability* is about the application of probability to modelling real-life situations. It follows the level 2 module M248 *Analysing data* and develops ideas about probability and random processes that are introduced there. Software for exploring properties of random processes is supplied as part of M343; its use is covered in the *Computer Book*.

This publication forms part of an Open University module. Details of this and other Open University modules can be obtained from the Student Registration and Enquiry Service, The Open University, PO Box 197, Milton Keynes MK7 6BJ, United Kingdom (tel. +44 (0)845 300 60 90; email general-enquiries@open.ac.uk).

Alternatively, you may visit the Open University website at www.open.ac.uk where you can learn more about the wide range of modules and packs offered at all levels by The Open University.

To purchase a selection of Open University materials visit www.ouw.co.uk, or contact Open University Worldwide, Walton Hall, Milton Keynes MK7 6AA, United Kingdom for a brochure (tel. +44 (0)1908 858793; fax +44 (0)1908 858787; email ouw-customer-services@open.ac.uk).

The Open University, Walton Hall, Milton Keynes MK7 6AA.

First published 2012.

Edited, designed and typeset by The Open University, using the Open University TEX System.

Printed in the United Kingdom by Henry Ling Limited at the Dorset Press Dorchester, DT1 1HD

ISBN 978 1 8487 3412 8

1.1

Contents

Study guide 5

Introduction 5

Part I Random processes 6
Introduction to Part I 6

1 What is a random process? 6
1.1 Basic ideas 6
1.2 The Bernoulli process 9

2 Further examples 12

Part II Modelling events in time 17
Introduction to Part II 17

3 The Poisson process 17
3.1 Basic ideas and results 20
3.2 Notation for continuous-time processes 22
3.3 Simulation 23

4 A more formal approach to the Poisson process 25

5 The multivariate Poisson process 31

6 The non-homogeneous Poisson process 34
6.1 The model 34
6.2 Basic results 36
6.3 Simulation 40

7 The compound Poisson process 44

8 Point processes 49
8.1 The index of dispersion 49
8.2 Types of point process 51

Part III Patterns in space 53
Introduction to Part III 53

9 Spatial patterns 54

10 Random patterns in space 59
10.1 The two-dimensional Bernoulli process 60
10.2 The two-dimensional Poisson process 60
10.3 Simulation for Poisson processes 62

11 Non-random spatial patterns 67
11.1 Patterns with regularity 67
11.2 Patterns with clustering 70

12 Counts and distances **72**
12.1 Counts of objects and their properties 73
12.2 Object-to-object and point-to-object distances 75

13 Detecting departures from randomness **80**
13.1 A test based on counts 80
13.2 A test based on distances 85
13.3 Significance testing 87
13.4 Postscript 89

14 Exercises on Book 2 **91**
14.1 Routine exercises 91
14.2 Further exercises 93

Summary of Book 2 **95**
Learning outcomes 96

Solutions to Activities **97**

Solutions to Exercises **106**

Acknowledgements **114**

Index **115**

Study guide

Each section of this book depends on ideas and results from the preceding sections, so we recommend that you study them in sequential order. The sections are of varying length. In Part I, both sections are shorter than average. In Part II, Section 6 is longer than average and Sections 5, 7 and 8 are quite short. In Part III, Sections 9 and 11 are shorter than average.

As you study this book, you will be asked to work through one chapter of the computer book. We recommend that you work through it at the point indicated in the text – in Section 6.

You should schedule eleven study sessions for this book. This includes time for working through one chapter of the computer book, and for answering the TMA and CMA questions and consolidating your work on this book. You should schedule one study session for Part I, six for Part II and four for Part III.

One possible study pattern is as follows.

Part I

Study session 1: Sections 1 and 2.

Part II

Study session 2: Section 3.

Study session 3: Sections 4 and 5.

Study session 4: TMA questions on Sections 1 to 5.

Study session 5: Section 6. You will need access to your computer for this session, together with the computer book.

Study session 6: Sections 7 and 8.

Study session 7: TMA questions on Sections 6 to 8.

Part III

Study session 8: Sections 9 and 10.

Study session 9: Sections 11 and 12.

Study session 10: Section 13.

Study session 11: TMA and CMA questions on Part III, and consolidating your work on this book.

Introduction

Many events occur in a random, unpredictable way. For example, air crashes, floods and earthquakes may occur at any time, prizes may be won by a gambler on the British national lottery in any draw, faults may occur at any point in a length of yarn, and dandelions may develop and flower at any point in a lawn. This book is concerned with modelling the patterns formed by events occurring in time and by objects located in space.

In Part I, you will learn what is meant by the term *random process*. Several examples are described, and some terminology and notation are introduced. Part II is devoted to models for events that occur in time. Models for patterns in space are discussed in Part III.

Part I Random processes

Introduction to Part I

In Part I, the fundamental ideas of random processes are introduced through a series of examples. The notation for random processes is discussed in Section 1, and some further examples are described in Section 2.

1 What is a random process?

In this section, the basic ideas of random processes and the notation used to represent them are introduced. Several examples are described in Subsection 1.1, and the Bernoulli process is discussed in Subsection 1.2.

1.1 Basic ideas

Examples 1.1 to 1.4 illustrate some fundamental ideas concerning random processes.

Example 1.1 The gambler's ruin

Two players, Adam and Ben, with initial capital £k and £$(a-k)$, respectively (where a and k are positive integers and $a > k$), engage in a series of games that involve some element of chance. After each game, the loser pays the winner £1. The series of games continues until one player has lost all his money, in which case he is said to be ruined.

This situation can be described in terms of a sequence of random variables. Let X_n represent Adam's capital (in £) after n games. The series of games ends when either $X_n = 0$ (in which case Adam is ruined) or $X_n = a$ (Ben is ruined). Suppose that $k = 4$ and $a = 7$, and that Adam's capital at the start and after each subsequent game is given by the sequence

$$4, 5, 6, 5, 4, 3, 4, 5, 6, 5, 6, 7.$$

This is a **realisation** of the sequence of random variables $\{X_n\}$ for $n = 0, 1, \ldots, 11$. In this case the series of games ends when Ben is ruined after the eleventh game.

If Adam and Ben had played again, the results of their games would probably have produced a different sequence of values from the one given above; that is, a different realisation of the sequence of random variables $\{X_n\}$ would have been obtained. Note that the distribution of each X_n (other than X_0) depends on chance. It also depends on the value of X_{n-1}: for example, if $X_{n-1} = 4$, then the value of X_n can be only either 3 or 5. ♦

The sequence of random variables $\{X_n; n = 0, 1, \ldots\}$ described in Example 1.1 is an example of a **random process** or **stochastic process**. Essentially, a random process is a sequence of random variables that is developing, usually over time, though as you will see later, it can be developing in space. The term 'random process' is also used for the whole underlying situation that is being observed.

The word 'stochastic' is derived from a Greek word meaning 'to aim at'. The evolution of its meaning is uncertain, but it now means 'pertaining to chance' or 'random'. It is pronounced sto-kas-tic.

In Example 1.1, Adam's capital was observed only at specific instants of time, immediately after each game had been completed. A process that is observed continuously during an interval of time is described in Example 1.2.

Example 1.2 *Customers in a village shop*

For two hours, a record was kept of the number of customers in a village shop. Figure 1.1 shows the number of customers in the shop at time t $(0 \le t \le 2)$, where t is measured in hours.

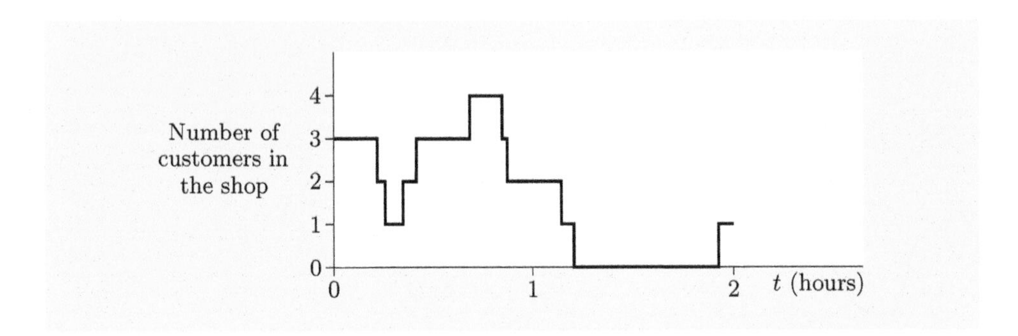

Figure 1.1 The number of customers in a shop

Each rise in the graph represents a customer arriving, and each fall, a customer leaving. At the start of the period of observation, there were three customers in the shop, and during the second hour there was a period of about 40 minutes when the shop was empty.

This example is a particular case of a *queueing process*; such processes are studied in *Book 4*.

If a record had been kept at the same time of day on another day, it would almost certainly have been different from the one represented in Figure 1.1: it would have been a different realisation of the stream of random variables $\{X(t); 0 \le t \le 2\}$, where $X(t)$ is the number of customers in the shop at time t. On each occasion that such records are kept, a realisation is obtained of a developing situation – the number of customers in the shop at time t.

For any fixed t, the distribution of $X(t)$ will depend on several factors, such as the arrival rate of customers and the time a customer spends in the shop. It also depends on the starting value. For example, in the realisation shown in Figure 1.1, $X(0) = 3$, so it would be very unlikely that $X(0.01) = 0$, because it is unlikely that all three customers would leave in under a minute. On the other hand, if the shop had been empty at time 0, then it would be quite likely that $X(0.01) = 0$. ♦

In the gambler's ruin example, the process is observed only at specific points in time. This process is said to be a **discrete-time random process**. On the other hand, the number of customers in the village shop is a **random process in continuous time**. In both of the examples, the random variables have taken only discrete non-negative integer values. Two processes for which the random variables are continuous are described in Examples 1.3 and 1.4.

Example 1.3 *Replacing light bulbs*

Suppose that there is a supply of light bulbs whose lifetimes are independent and identically distributed. One bulb is used at a time, and as soon as it fails it is replaced by a new one. Let W_n represent the time at which the nth bulb fails and is replaced. Then the random process $\{W_n; n = 1, 2, \ldots\}$ gives the sequence of replacement times. Note that the 'time' variable in this example is n, the number of the bulb, so this is a discrete-time random process. However, the lifetime of a bulb is a continuous random variable, so W_n, the replacement time of the nth light bulb, is continuous. ♦

This is an example of a *renewal process*; such processes are discussed in *Book 5*.

Example 1.4 The water level in a reservoir

The level of water in a reservoir depends on supply, in the form of rain or melting snow, on demand, which is the water used by the community served by the reservoir, and on other minor factors, such as evaporation from the surface. Both supply and demand may be assumed to be continuous random variables. Let $L(t)$ be a random variable representing the level of water in the reservoir at time t, where t is measured in years. The level of the reservoir can be observed at any time $t \geq 0$, so $\{L(t); t \geq 0\}$ is a continuous-time random process. A typical realisation of the process $\{L(t); t \geq 0\}$ is shown in Figure 1.2.

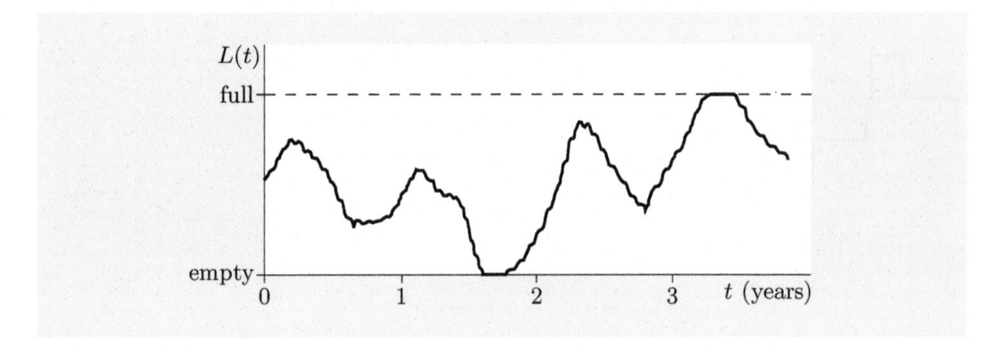

Figure 1.2 A realisation of $\{L(t); t \geq 0\}$, where $L(t)$ is the water level in a reservoir

The water level $L(t)$ tends to reach a maximum around March after the winter rain, and to fall to a minimum in the autumn, because there is more demand (watering gardens, etc.) in the summer, but less supply. However, there is variation from year to year. The water level may fall to zero in a drought or remain at a maximum for a period of time when the reservoir is full and an overflow is in operation. In this example, the random variable $L(t)$ is continuous and the random process develops in continuous time. ♦

Mathematically, a random process is a collection $\{X(t)\}$ or $\{X_n\}$ of random variables defined in either continuous time or discrete time. For a random process in continuous time, the time variable is usually defined for an interval of the real line, most commonly $-\infty < t < \infty$ or $t \geq 0$, in which case the collection is written as $\{X(t); t \in \mathbb{R}\}$ or $\{X(t); t \geq 0\}$. The range of t is called the **time domain**. For a random process in discrete time, the time variable is usually defined at integer points, and the process is written as $\{X_n; n = 0, 1, 2, \ldots\}$. In this case, the time domain is $\{0, 1, 2, \ldots\}$. Thus typically a random process with a discrete time domain is written as $\{X_n; n = 0, 1, 2, \ldots\}$, and a random process with a continuous time domain is written as $\{X(t); t \geq 0\}$.

The set of values that may be taken by the random variables in a random process is called the **state space** of the process. A state space can be either discrete or continuous. In Example 1.2, $X(t)$ is the number of customers in a village shop at time t, so the state space of $\{X(t); 0 \leq t \leq 2\}$ is $\{0, 1, 2, \ldots\}$. The state space is discrete in this example. In Example 1.4, $L(t)$ is the level of water in a reservoir, which is a continuous non-negative variate, so the state space of $\{L(t); t \geq 0\}$ is $\{l : l \geq 0\}$. The state space is continuous in this example.

Activity 1.1 Time domains and state spaces

For each of the random processes described in Examples 1.1 and 1.3, identify the time domain and say whether it is discrete or continuous. Also write down the state space and say whether it is discrete or continuous.

Activity 1.2 More time domains and state spaces

A shop is open between 9 am and 6 pm on weekdays. Two random processes associated with the daily business of the shop are as follows.

(a) $\{A_n; n = 1, 2, \ldots\}$, where A_n is the amount (in £) spent by the nth customer who enters the shop during the day.

(b) $\{B(t); 0 \leq t \leq 9\}$, where $B(t)$ is the number of items sold by t hours after the shop opens.

For each process, identify the time domain and say whether it is discrete or continuous. Also write down the state space and say whether it is discrete or continuous.

1.2 The Bernoulli process

The term **Bernoulli trial** is used to describe a single statistical experiment in which there are two possible outcomes; these outcomes are referred to as 'success' and 'failure'. A sequence of independent Bernoulli trials for which the probability of success remains constant from trial to trial is called a **Bernoulli process**. The formal definition of a Bernoulli process is given in the following box.

Bernoulli process

A **Bernoulli process** is a sequence of Bernoulli trials in which:

◇ trials are independent;

◇ the probability of success remains the same from trial to trial.

Examples of Bernoulli processes include: a sequence of rolls of a die where success is a 'six'; testing items off a production line where success is a 'good' item and failure is a defective item; and treating successive patients arriving at a hospital where success is a 'cure'.

For a Bernoulli process, the idea of trials occurring in order, one after the other, is crucial.

There are several different sequences of random variables associated with a Bernoulli process. The simplest one is $\{X_n; n = 1, 2, \ldots\}$, where $X_n = 1$ if the nth trial results in success, and $X_n = 0$ if it is a failure. Each X_n has a Bernoulli distribution with parameter p, the probability of success at any trial. The random variables $X_1, X_2, \ldots$ are independent and identically distributed, and the distribution of X_n does not depend on n or on the results of previous trials.

The 'time' variable, n, is discrete; it denotes the number of the trial. The random variables are also discrete-valued; the state space is $\{0, 1\}$. Therefore the random process $\{X_n; n = 1, 2, \ldots\}$ has a discrete time domain and a discrete state space.

The real time variable, the time between trials, is not considered in a Bernoulli process; it is irrelevant, for example, exactly when patients arrive at the hospital.

A typical realisation of the process $\{X_n; n = 1, 2, \ldots\}$ is

$$0, 0, 0, 1, 0, 1, 1, 0, 1, 1, 1, 0, 0.$$

In this realisation, successes occur at trials 4, 6, 7, 9, 10 and 11, and failures at the other trials. In this realisation there were 13 trials.

Another sequence of random variables associated with a Bernoulli process is $\{Y_n; n = 1, 2, \ldots\}$, where

$$Y_n = X_1 + X_2 + \cdots + X_n.$$

This sequence specifies the number of successes that have occurred after n trials have been completed. The realisation of the sequence $\{Y_n; n = 1, 2, \ldots, 13\}$ corresponding to the realisation of $\{X_n; n = 1, 2, \ldots, 13\}$ is

$$0, 0, 0, 1, 1, 2, 3, 3, 4, 5, 6, 6, 6.$$

This realisation is represented in Figure 1.3.

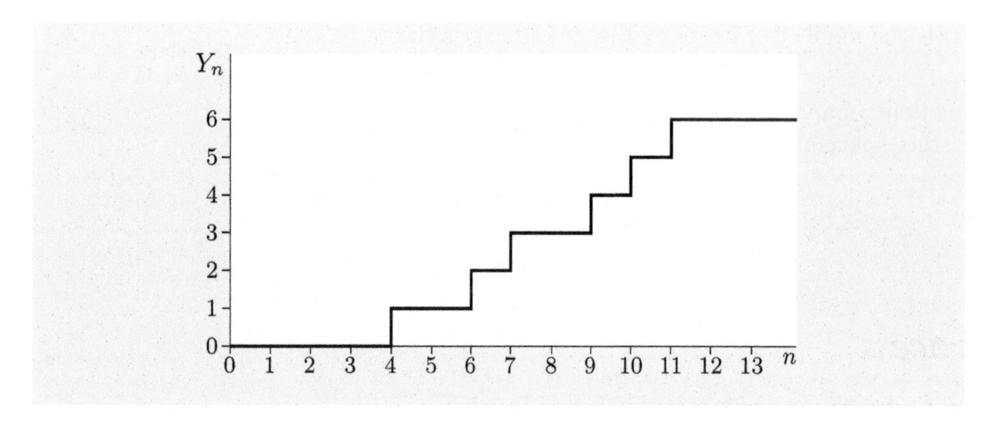

Figure 1.3 A realisation of $\{Y_n; n = 1, 2, \ldots, 13\}$ from a Bernoulli process

Note that, since the random variable Y_n is discrete, the graph of any realisation of the sequence $\{Y_n; n = 1, 2, \ldots\}$ appears as an increasing step function.

Activity 1.3 The distribution of Y_n

(a) What is the unconditional distribution of Y_n?

(b) Specify the conditional distribution of Y_n given $Y_{n-1} = y$.

Activity 1.4 Another sequence

Suggest a third sequence of random variables associated with a Bernoulli process – that is, another random process. You should use the notation for random processes in your answer. Write down the distribution of the random variables in the sequence.

Say whether the time domain of your random process is discrete or continuous, write down the state space, and say whether the state space is discrete or continuous.

Example 1.5 The British national lottery

A gambler who buys a single ticket each Saturday for the British national lottery has probability $p = 1/13\,983\,816$ of winning the jackpot (or a share of it) each week. This probability is unaltered from Saturday to Saturday, and what happens on any Saturday is independent of what has occurred on previous Saturdays. The Bernoulli random variable X_n is defined to take the value 1 if the gambler wins the jackpot at the nth attempt, and 0 otherwise. Then over a period of (say) 20 Saturdays, the random process $\{X_n; n = 1, 2, \ldots, 20\}$ is a discrete-valued discrete-time random process that may be modelled by a Bernoulli process with parameter p. ♦

Example 1.6 Births of boys and girls in a family

At first sight, a Bernoulli process might appear to be a useful model for the sequence of boys and girls in a family – scoring 1 for a girl, say, and 0 for a boy. Then a family of five with four sisters and a baby brother might be represented by the sequence $1, 1, 1, 1, 0$. The probability p of a female child may be estimated from data.

For some purposes, the model may be adequate. Indeed, departures from the two defining assumptions of the Bernoulli process are typically rather hard to detect. But extended analyses of available data suggest that the assumption of independence from birth to birth is not valid. Nature has a kind of memory, and the gender of a previous child affects to some degree the probability distribution for the gender of a subsequent child. ♦

Activity 1.5 Modelling the weather

Observers classified each day in a three-week interval as either 'Wet' or 'Dry' according to some rule for summarising the weather on any particular day. The 21-day sequence was as follows.

Wet Wet Wet Dry Dry Wet Wet Dry Wet Wet Wet
Wet Dry Dry Dry Wet Wet Wet Dry Dry Dry

Scoring 1 for a wet day and 0 for a dry day, the sequence may be written more conveniently as

1 1 1 0 0 1 1 0 1 1 1 1 0 0 0 1 1 1 0 0 0.

This is a realisation of the random process $\{X_n; n = 1, 2, \ldots, 21\}$, where the random variable X_n is discrete and takes the value 0 or 1, so that X_n is a Bernoulli random variable.

The time variable n denotes the number of the day in the sequence. Thus the random process $\{X_n; n = 1, 2, \ldots\}$ has a discrete time domain and a discrete state space.

Explain whether or not a Bernoulli process is likely to be a good model for the daily weather.

Activity 1.5 raises an important point: probability models are not usually 'right' or 'wrong': they may be better described as adequate or inadequate. However, M343 is concerned primarily with the development and application of models, rather than with testing their adequacy.

Summary of Section 1

In this section, a random process has been defined to be a sequence of random variables, and the notation for random processes has been introduced. You have seen that the time domain and the state space of a random process can each be either discrete or continuous. The Bernoulli process has been discussed. It has been noted that the term 'random process' is used to describe a whole physical process as well as a sequence of random variables associated with a physical process.

2 Further examples

This section consists of further examples of random processes, many of which will be discussed in detail later in the module. At this stage, you are expected to note the type of situation that may be modelled by a random process, to become accustomed to identifying sequences of random variables, to recognise whether the time domain and the state space of a random process are discrete or continuous, and to practise using the notation for random processes.

Example 2.1 A ticket queue

Many probability models have been developed to describe various queueing situations. The simplest situation is that of a ticket queue at a box office where customers arrive and join the end of the queue; they eventually reach the front and are served, then they leave. Sometimes an arriving customer will find that there is no queue and is served immediately.

To define the queueing process completely, the arrival and service mechanisms must be specified. The commonest and simplest assumption is that customers arrive at random. Frequently, the service time is assumed to have an exponential distribution. ♦

Activity 2.1 Random processes for a queue

There are several random processes associated with the queueing model described in Example 2.1. The basic random process is $\{Q(t); t \geq 0\}$, where $Q(t)$ is the number of people in the queue at time t. Other processes include $\{L_n; n = 1, 2, \ldots\}$, where L_n is the number of people in the queue when the nth customer arrives, and $\{W_n; n = 1, 2, \ldots\}$, where W_n is the time that the nth customer has to wait before being served.

For each of these processes, say whether the time domain and the state space are discrete or continuous, and write down the state space.

The simple queueing model in Example 2.1 can be extended in many ways. Possibilities include having more than one server, arrival according to an appointments system, arrival of customers in batches, and 'baulking'. ('Baulking' is a term used to describe the phenomenon of a long queue discouraging customers from joining.)

Several *queueing processes* are developed and analysed in *Book 4*.

Example 2.2 Machine breakdowns

A machine can be in one of two states: working or under repair. As soon as it breaks down, work begins on repairing it; and as soon as the machine is repaired, it starts working again.

For $t \geq 0$, let $X(t)$ be a random variable such that $X(t) = 1$ if the machine is working and $X(t) = 0$ if it is under repair. Then the sequence $\{X(t); t \geq 0\}$ is a random process with continuous time domain and having the discrete state space $\{0, 1\}$. ♦

Activity 2.2 Another random process

Suggest another random process associated with the model for machine breakdowns described in Example 2.2. Say whether the time domain is discrete or continuous. Write down the state space and say whether it is discrete or continuous.

The model for machine breakdowns in Example 2.2 could be extended to include several machines, and questions could then be asked about how many machines are working at any time or how many mechanics are required to prevent a build up of broken-down machines. The model could include a third state: broken and awaiting repair.

Example 2.3 The card-collecting problem

With every petrol purchase, an oil company gives away a card portraying an important event in the history of the petroleum industry. There are 20 such cards, and on each occasion the probability of receiving any particular card is 1/20. For an individual customer, one sequence of random variables associated with this situation is $\{X_n; n = 1, 2, \ldots\}$, where $X_n = 1$ if the card received at his nth purchase is a new one for his collection, and $X_n = 0$ if his nth card is a replica of one he has already. Both the time domain and the state space are discrete. The state space is $\{0, 1\}$. ♦

Activity 2.3 Collecting cards

(a) Suppose that the customer in Example 2.3 has i different cards after $n - 1$ purchases. Write down the distribution of X_n in this case.

(b) Explain whether or not the card-collecting process is a Bernoulli process.

(c) Identify two other random processes (sequences of random variables) associated with the card-collecting process. For each sequence, say whether the time domain and the state space are discrete or continuous. In each case, give the state space.

Example 2.4 The weather

Suppose that, at a particular location, the weather is classified each day as either wet or dry according to some specific criterion – perhaps wet if at least 1 mm of rain is recorded, otherwise dry. Weather tends to go in spells of wet or dry, and a possible model is that the weather on any one day depends only on the weather the previous day. For example, if it rains today, then the probability that it will rain tomorrow is $\frac{3}{5}$, and the probability that it will be dry is $\frac{2}{5}$; on the other hand, if it is dry today, then the probability that it will be dry (wet) tomorrow is $\frac{7}{10}$ $\left(\frac{3}{10}\right)$.

This is an example of a *Markov chain*. Such models are discussed in *Book 3*.

The random variable X_n could be defined to take the value 0 if it is wet on day n, and 1 if it is dry on day n. The sequence $\{X_n; n = 0, 1, 2, \ldots\}$ is a random process with a discrete time domain and a discrete state space. The time domain is $\{0, 1, 2, \ldots\}$ and the state space is $\{0, 1\}$.

The sorts of question that arise include the following. If it is wet on Monday, what is the probability that it will be wet the following Thursday? What proportion of days will be wet in the long run? If it is wet today, how long is it likely to be before the next wet day? ♦

Activity 2.4 The weather model

The model described in Example 2.4 can be thought of as a sequence of trials. Explain why it is *not* a Bernoulli process.

Example 2.5 Family surnames

In a community, a surname is passed down from generation to generation through male offspring only. Suppose that each man has a number of sons. This number is a random variable taking the values $0, 1, 2, \ldots$. Each man reproduces independently of all others.

One ancestor (patriarch) has a number of sons who form the first generation. Each of these has sons who form the second generation, and so on. Let the random variable X_n represent the number of men in the nth generation, with $X_0 = 1$ denoting the original ancestor. Then $\{X_n; n = 0, 1, 2, \ldots\}$ is an example of a *branching process*. The time domain, which represents the generation number, is discrete. The state space is $\{0, 1, 2, \ldots\}$, which is also discrete.

Branching processes are discussed in *Book 3*.

The questions that are of interest include the following. What is the distribution of the size of the nth generation? And will the family surname survive, or will it eventually become extinct? ♦

Example 2.6 The spread of a disease

Suppose that an infectious disease is introduced into a community and spreads through it. At any time, each member of the community may be classified as belonging to just one of four categories: healthy but susceptible to the disease; having the disease and infectious; recovered and immune from a further attack; dead. These categories can be called S_1, S_2, S_3, S_4, respectively.

A person may pass from S_1 to S_2 after contact with someone in S_2. Anyone in S_2 will eventually go to either S_3 or S_4. Four sequences of random variables, $\{S_1(t); t \geq 0\}$, $\{S_2(t); t \geq 0\}$, $\{S_3(t); t \geq 0\}$, $\{S_4(t); t \geq 0\}$, can be defined, where $S_i(t)$ is the number of people in category S_i at time t. Each of these processes is defined for continuous time, and its state space is discrete. If the disease starts in a community of size N with a single infectious person, then $S_1(0) = N - 1$, $S_2(0) = 1$, $S_3(0) = 0$, $S_4(0) = 0$. If, at some time t, $S_2(t) = 0$, then the disease will spread no further. There is a relationship between the four variates: if no one enters or leaves the community, then $S_1(t) + S_2(t) + S_3(t) + S_4(t) = N$, the total size of the community.

To develop a model for this process, it is necessary to specify the mechanics of the spread of the disease, the probabilities that an infected person will recover or die, the time spent in various stages, and so on. ♦

This is an example of an *epidemic process*, for which several models are described in *Book 4*.

Activity 2.5 A population model

A colony of bacteria develops by the division (into two) of bacteria and by the death of bacteria. No bacterium joins or leaves the colony.

This is an example of a *birth and death process.* Such processes are analysed in *Book 4*.

(a) Identify two random processes to describe the development of this colony, and in each case specify whether the state space and the time domain are discrete or continuous. Write down the state space for each process.

(b) Suppose that the colony starts with two bacteria. Sketch a possible realisation of the size of the colony over time.

Example 2.7 The price of wheat

In an article published in 1953, Professor Sir Maurice Kendall considers wheat prices in Chicago, measured in cents per bushel at weekly intervals from January 1883 to September 1934 (with a gap during the war years). A portion of these data is shown in Figure 2.1.

Kendall, M.G. (1953) 'The analysis of economic time-series, Part I: Prices', *Journal of the Royal Statistical Society, Series A*, vol. 116, no. 1, pp. 11–34.

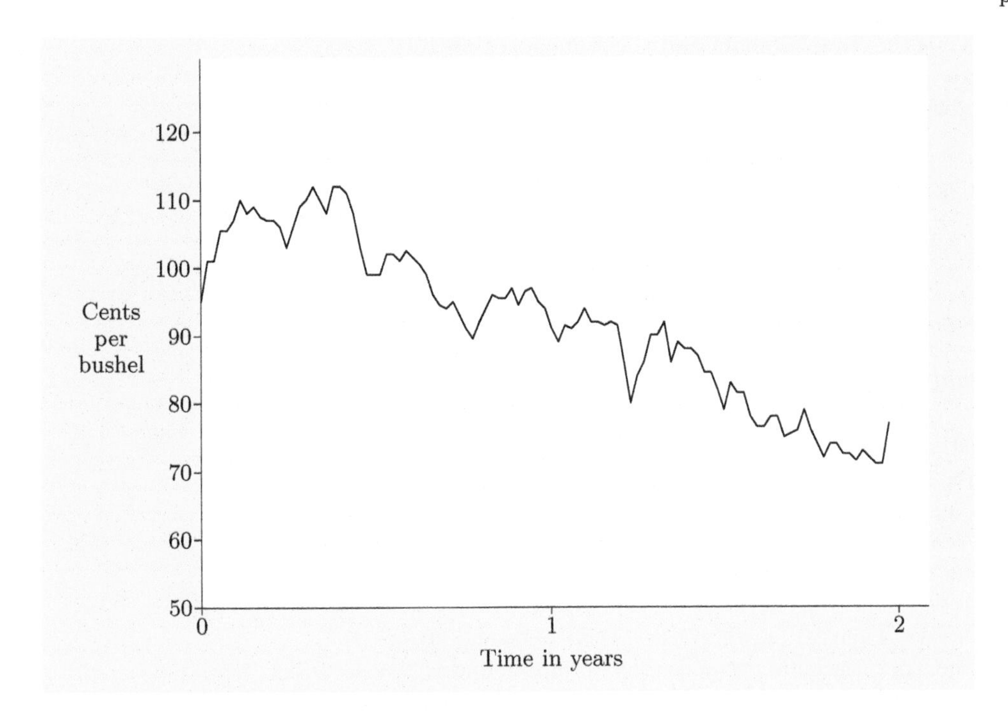

Figure 2.1 The price of wheat in Chicago

There is an overall fall in the price over the two-year period shown in the graph. However, as Kendall reported, first impressions are 'almost as if once a week the Demon of Chance drew a random number ... and added it to the current price to determine the next week's price'. Although observed only once a week, the price of wheat could change at any time, and the price itself varies continuously (though rounded to the nearest cent). The random process $\{Q(t); t \geq 0\}$, where $Q(t)$ is the price of wheat at time t, is therefore an example of a random process where both the time domain and the state space are continuous; it is an example of a *diffusion process.* ♦

This and other diffusion processes are studied in *Book 5*.

Example 2.8 The thickness of wool yarn

The thickness of wool yarn is not uniform along the length of the yarn. Figure 2.2 shows the variation in weight per unit length (essentially, the variation in cross-sectional area) along a strand of wool yarn.

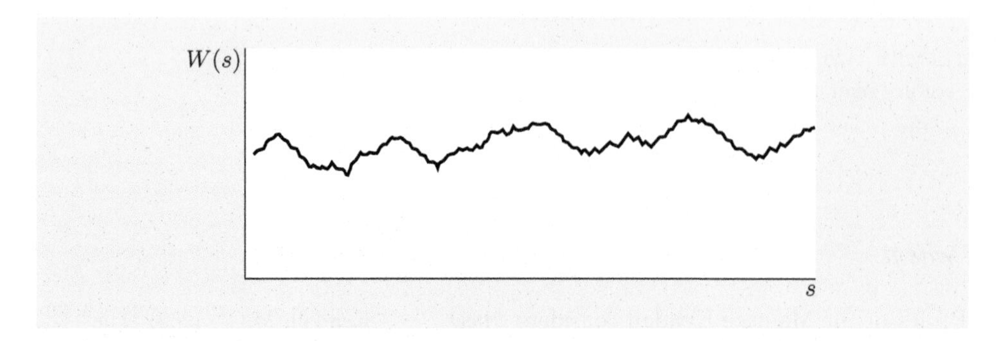

Figure 2.2 Variation of weight per unit length along a strand of wool yarn

The length s along the yarn corresponds to the time variable t that has appeared in previous examples, and is continuous. The random variable $W(s)$, weight per unit length, is also continuous. Thus the 'time' domain and the state space of the random process $\{W(s); s \geq 0\}$ are both continuous. This is an example of a random process developing over distance instead of time. ♦

Random processes in space are discussed in Part III of this book. Random processes in two-dimensional space, where a process develops over an area of land, arise frequently in biology and geology. One such process is described in Example 2.9.

Example 2.9 The bee orchid

Pingle Wood and Cutting is a nature reserve on the route of the now disused Great Eastern Railway line between March and St Ives. It is owned by The Wildlife Trust, and bee orchids can be found there in June. In any year, the distribution of the orchid in the reserve can be thought of as a random process in two-dimensional space. Each point can be identified as (x, y) according to a map reference, and a random variable X is defined by $X(x, y) = 1$ if an orchid grows at that point, and $X(x, y) = 0$ otherwise. Then $\{X(x, y); x \in \mathbb{R}, y \in \mathbb{R}\}$ is a random process where the equivalent of the 'time' variable actually refers to space and is two-dimensional and continuous. The state space is $\{0, 1\}$, which is discrete.

Naturalists might be interested in questions such as the following. Does the orchid grow randomly in the reserve or does it favour certain soil types or south-sloping land? Does it grow singly or in clumps? To answer such questions, a model would have to be set up, and the data collected and compared with the model. ♦

Summary of Section 2

In this section, a variety of examples of random processes have been described briefly. Some of these will be discussed in detail in M343. In most of the examples, the process was developing over time. However, you have seen that it is also possible to have a random process that develops in space.

Part II Modelling events in time

Introduction to Part II

In Part II, several models for events that occur in time are described, and the properties of these models are discussed. In Section 3, a model is described that is appropriate for events occurring 'at random' in such a way that their rate of occurrence remains constant. This model is known as the *Poisson process.* The main results quoted without proof in Section 3 are derived in Section 4 using a mathematical approach. This approach is fundamental to much of the work in *Book 4*.

The Poisson process model is extended in several ways in Sections 5 to 7 – to include events of several types, events occurring at a rate that varies with time, and multiple events. A technique that may be used to compare some random processes with a Poisson process is introduced in Section 8.

3 The Poisson process

Some data on major earthquakes that occurred in the 20th century are described in Example 3.1.

Example 3.1 *Earthquakes*

Table 3.1 contains a list of the most serious earthquakes that occurred in the 20th century up to 1977, and includes the date and place of occurrence, the magnitude of the earthquake and the estimated number of fatalities. The magnitude of an earthquake is measured on the Richter scale and relates to the energy released.

Table 3.1 Major earthquakes in the 20th century up to 1977

An earthquake is included if its magnitude was at least 7.5 or if a thousand or more people were killed.

These data are from the discontinued Open University module S237 *The Earth: structure, composition and evolution*, Block 2.

Date			Magnitude (if known)	Region	Estimated number of fatalities
1902	Dec	16		Turkestan	4 500
1905	Apr	4	8.6	India: Kangra	19 000
	Sept	8		Italy: Calabria	2 500
1906	Jan	31	8.9	Colombia	1 000
	Mar	16		Formosa: Kagi	1 300
	Apr	18	8.3	California: San Francisco	700
	Aug	17	8.6	Chile: Santiago, Valparaiso	20 000
1907	Jan	14		Jamaica: Kingston	1 600
	Oct	21	8.1	Central Asia	12 000
1908	Dec	28	7.5	Italy: Messina, Reggio	83 000
1911	Jan	3	8.7	China: Tien-Shan	450
1912	Aug	9	7.8	Marmara Sea	1 950
1915	Jan	13	7.0	Italy: Avezzano	29 980
	Oct	3	7.6	California, Nevada	0
1920	Dec	16	8.6	China: Kansu, Shansi	100 000
1922	Nov	11	8.4	Peru: Atacama	600
1923	Sept	1	8.3	Japan: Tokyo, Yokohama	143 000
1925	Mar	16	7.1	China: Yunnan	5 000
1927	Mar	7	7.9	Japan: Tango	3 020
	May	22	8.3	China: Nan-Shan	200 000
1929	May	1	7.1	Iran: Shirwan	3 300
	June	16	7.8	New Zealand: Buller	17
1930	July	23	6.5	Italy: Ariano, Melfi	1 430
1931	Feb	2	7.9	New Zealand: Hawke's Bay	255
1933	Mar	2	8.9	Japan: Morioka	2 990
1934	Jan	15	8.4	India: Bihar-Nepal	10 700
1935	Apr	20	7.1	Formosa	3 280
	May	30	7.5	Pakistan: Quetta	30 000
1939	Jan	25	8.3	Chile: Talca	28 000
	Dec	26	7.9	Turkey: Erzincan	30 000
1943	Sept	10	7.4	Japan: Tottori	1 190
1944	Dec	7	8.3	Japan: Tonankai, Nankaido	1 000
1945	Jan	12	7.1	Japan: Mikawa	1 900
1946	Nov	10	7.4	Peru: Ancash	1 400
	Dec	20	8.4	Japan: Tonankai, Nankaido	1 330
1948	June	28	7.3	Japan: Fukui	5 390
	Oct	5	7.6	Turkmenia, Ashkhabad	Unknown
1949	Aug	5	6.8	Ecuador: Ambato	6 000
1950	Aug	15	8.7	India, Assam, Tibet	1 530
1952	Mar	4	8.6	Japan: Tokachi	28
	July	21	7.7	California: Kern County	11
1954	Sept	9	6.8	Algeria: Orléansville	1 250
1955	Mar	31	7.9	Phillipines: Mindanao	430
1956	June	9	7.7	Afghanistan: Kabul	220
	July	9	7.7	Aegean Sea: Santorini	57
1957	July	28	7.8	Mexico: Acapulco	55
	Dec	4	8.0	Mongolia: Altai-Gobi	30
	Dec	13	7.1	Iran: Farsinaj, Hamadan	1 130
1958	July	10	7.8	Alaska, Brit. Columbia, Yukon	5
1960	Feb	29	5.8	Morocco: Agadir	14 000
	May	22	8.5	Chile: Valdivia	5 700
1962	Sept	1	7.3	Iran: Qazvin	12 230
1963	July	26	6.0	Yugoslavia: Skopje	1 200
1964	Mar	28	8.5	Alaska: Anchorage, Seward	178
1968	Aug	31	7.4	Iran: Dasht-e Bayaz	11 600
1970	May	31	7.8	Peru: Nr Lima	66 000
1972	Dec	23	6.2	Nicaragua: Managua	5 000
1974	Dec	28	6.2	Pakistan: Pattan	5 300
1975	Feb	4	7.5	China: Haicheng, Liaoning	Few
1976	Feb	4	7.9	Guatemala	22 000
	May	6	6.5	Italy: Gemona, Friuli	1 000
	July	27	7.6	China: Tangshan	650 000
1977	Mar	4	7.2	Romania: Vrancea	2 000

Seismologists would study these data with specific objectives in mind. They might wish to study the structure of the Earth or to predict future earthquakes, for example. In this section, the times of occurrence will be studied. In order to do this, the times (in days) between successive earthquakes have been calculated; these are shown in Table 3.2. (The numbers should be read down the columns.)

Table 3.2 Times between major earthquakes (in days)

840	280	695	402	335	99	436	83	735
157	434	294	194	1354	304	30	832	38
145	736	562	759	454	375	384	328	365
44	584	721	319	36	567	129	246	92
33	887	76	460	667	139	9	1617	82
121	263	710	40	40	780	209	638	220
150	1901	46	1336	556	203	599	937	

These times range from 9 days up to 1901 days (which is over five years), so they have a very large variance. It is difficult to appreciate a pattern from studying a list of figures, so in order to develop some intuition about the pattern, the data are presented in two ways in Figures 3.1 and 3.2.

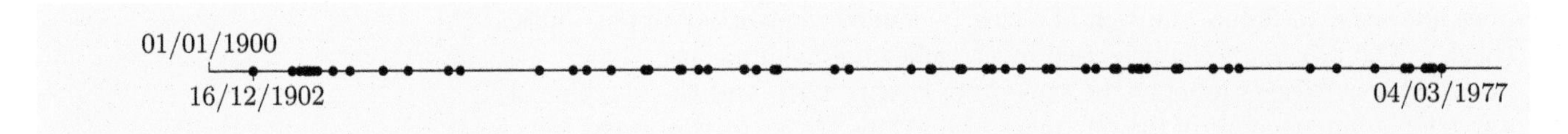

Figure 3.1 Times at which major earthquakes occurred, measured in days

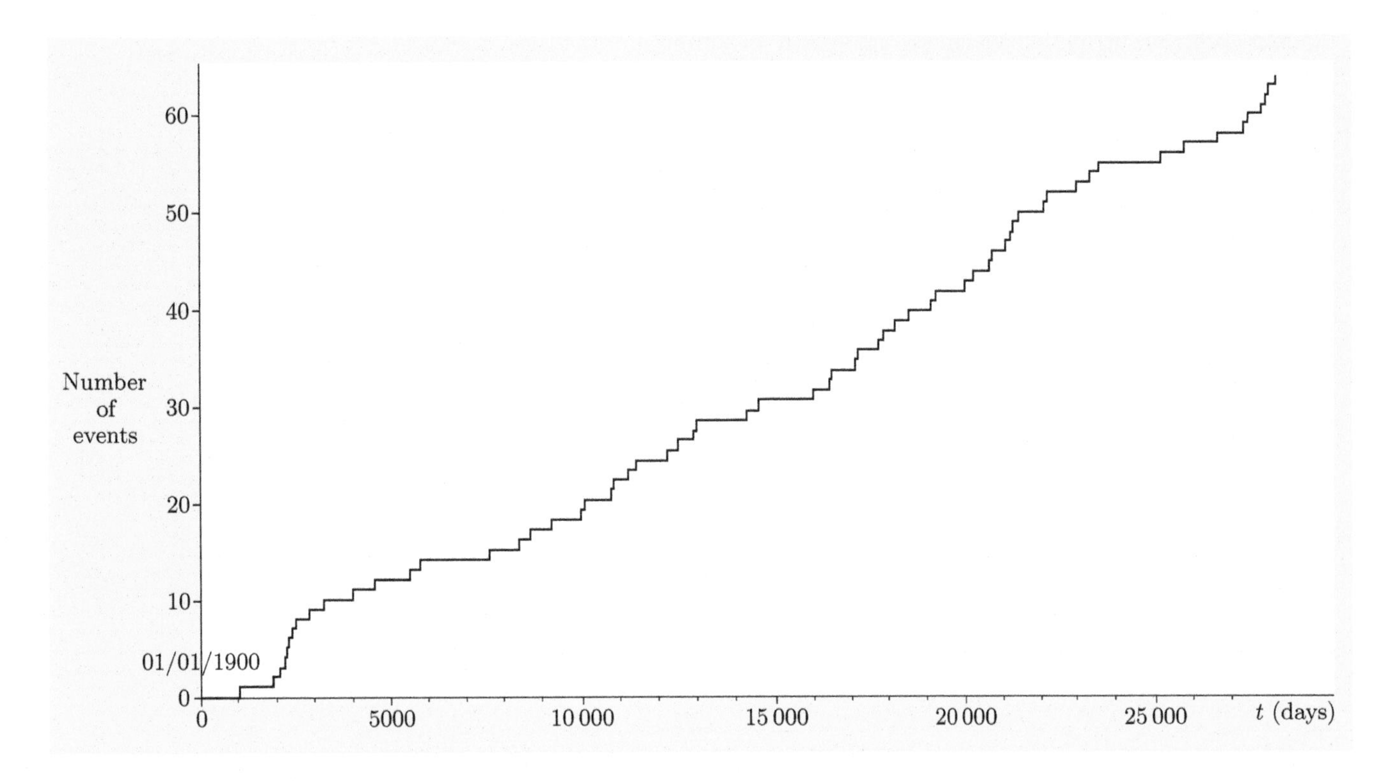

Figure 3.2 Cumulative number of earthquakes over time

In Figure 3.1, dots on a time axis show the incidence of earthquakes over the period of observation. Figure 3.2 gives a cumulative count with passing time.

The trend in Figure 3.2 could be approximated very roughly by a straight line; there is no pronounced curvature. This suggests that the rate of occurrence of earthquakes has remained more or less steady. However, the random element in the sequence of earthquake times is evident from both figures, and this is the element for which a model is required. ♦

In this section, a model that might be suitable for the occurrence of major earthquakes is described. This model is the **Poisson process**. It is a model for events occurring at random for which the rate of occurrence of events remains constant over time. In Subsection 3.1, the Poisson process is defined and some basic ideas and results are discussed. Some standard notation for events occurring in continuous time is introduced in Subsection 3.2. The simulation of events in a Poisson process is discussed briefly in Subsection 3.3.

3.1 Basic ideas and results

The Poisson process is the continuous-time analogue of the Bernoulli process. In a Poisson process, events occur 'at random', but instead of occurring as a result of regular trials, as in the Bernoulli process, they can occur at any time. The Poisson process provides a good model for such varied situations as the decay of radioactive atoms in a lump of material, the times of arrival of customers to join a queue, the instants at which cars pass a point on a road in free-flowing traffic, and the times of goals scored in a soccer match.

The Bernoulli process is a useful model when an event either occurs (a success) or does not occur (a failure) at each of a clearly defined sequence of opportunities (trials). The process is characterised by the following assumptions: the probability of success remains the same from trial to trial, and the outcome at any trial is independent of the outcomes of previous trials. In this sense, the sequence of successes and failures is quite haphazard.

Events may also occur in a random, haphazard kind of a way in continuous time, when there is no notion of a 'trial' or 'opportunity'. Examples of unforecastable random events occurring in continuous time (with an estimate of the rate at which they might happen) include the following:

- machine breakdowns on the factory floor (one every five days);
- light bulb failures in the home (one every three months);
- arrivals at a hospital casualty ward (one every ten minutes at peak time);
- major earthquakes worldwide (one every fourteen months);
- power cuts in the home ('frequently' in winter, 'seldom' in summer).

Typically, a realisation of this sort of random process is represented as a sequence of points plotted on a time axis, as in Figure 3.3, the points giving the times of occurrence.

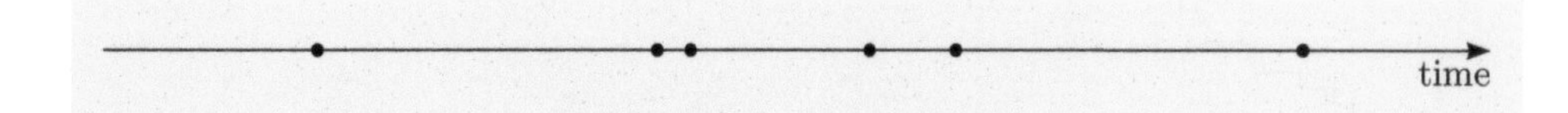

Figure 3.3 Schematic representation of a random sequence of events in time

The Poisson process is defined in the following box.

Poisson process

The **Poisson process** is a model for the occurrence of events in continuous time in which the following assumptions are made.

- Events occur singly.
- The rate of occurrence of events remains constant.
- The incidence of future events is independent of the past.

Consider, for instance, the occurrence of light bulb failures in the home. Failures might be well (or at least adequately) modelled by a Poisson process: they never (or rarely) happen simultaneously and there is no particular reason why the rate at which they occur should vary with passing time. Perhaps it is just arguable that the incidence of past events provides indicators for the future. But remember that few models are 'right'; most are adequate, at best. And a Poisson process may be an adequate model for failures for the purpose of determining, say, the stock of light bulbs to keep in the home.

On the other hand, the incidence of power cuts in the home would not be well modelled by a Poisson process: the rate is greater in winter than in summer, so the second assumption is not reasonable in this case.

Two random variables are of particular interest for the Poisson process: the number of events that occur over any particular period of observation (for example, breakdowns in a month), which is a discrete random variable; and the time between successive events (or 'waiting time' between successive events, as it is often called), which is a continuous random variable. The distributions of these random variables are stated in the following box.

Poisson process: two main results

Suppose that events occur at random at rate λ in such a way that their occurrence may be modelled as a Poisson process. Then:

- ◇ $N(t)$, the number of events that occur during an interval of length t, has a Poisson distribution with parameter λt: $N(t) \sim \text{Poisson}(\lambda t)$;
- ◇ T, the waiting time between successive events, has an exponential distribution with parameter λ: $T \sim M(\lambda)$.

These two results are derived in Section 4. Their use is illustrated in Example 3.2.

Example 3.2 Arrivals at a casualty department

Suppose that over moderately short intervals, the incidence of patients arriving at a casualty department may usefully be modelled as a Poisson process in time with (on average) 10 minutes between arrivals.

Since the mean time between arrivals is 10 minutes, the rate of the Poisson process is

$$\lambda = \tfrac{1}{10} \text{ per minute.}$$

Therefore the number of arrivals in half an hour has a Poisson distribution with parameter

$$\lambda t = \tfrac{1}{10} \text{ per minute} \times 30 \text{ minutes} = 3.$$

That is,

$$N(30) \sim \text{Poisson}(3).$$

The probability that two patients arrive in half an hour is

$$P(N(30) = 2) = \frac{e^{-3}3^2}{2!} \simeq 0.2240.$$

If $X \sim \text{Poisson}(3)$, then

$$P(X = x) = \frac{e^{-3}3^x}{x!}$$

for $x = 0, 1, \ldots$.

The waiting time between arrivals has an exponential distribution with parameter $\frac{1}{10}$, so the probability that the interval between arrivals exceeds half an hour is given by $P(T > 30)$.

The c.d.f. of T is

$$F(t) = P(T \leq t) = 1 - e^{-\lambda t}, \quad t \geq 0,$$

so

$$P(T > t) = e^{-\lambda t}.$$

Therefore

$$P(T > 30) = e^{-30/10} = e^{-3} \simeq 0.0498. \quad ♦$$

Activity 3.1 Nerve impulses

In a psychological experiment, nerve impulses were found to occur at the rate of 458 impulses per second. Assume that a Poisson process is a suitable model for the incidence of impulses.

(a) Calculate the probability that not more than one nerve impulse occurs in an interval of $\frac{1}{100}$ second.

(b) Calculate the probability that the interval between two successive impulses is less than $\frac{1}{1000}$ second.

Activity 3.2 Major earthquakes

Suppose that the incidence of major earthquakes worldwide may be adequately modelled as a Poisson process, and that earthquakes occur at the rate of one every fourteen months.

(a) Calculate the probability that there will be at least three major earthquakes in a period of ten years.

(b) Calculate the probability that the waiting time between successive major earthquakes exceeds two years.

3.2 Notation for continuous-time processes

Events in an interval

For *any* continuous-time process where successive events are counted, the number of events that occur between times t_1 and t_2 is denoted $X(t_1, t_2)$.

A realisation of a continuous-time process is depicted in Figure 3.4.

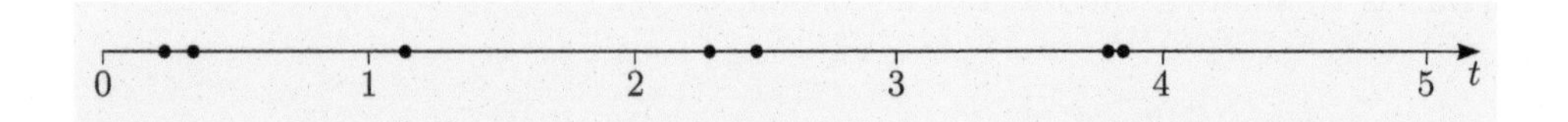

Figure 3.4 Events in a continuous-time process

In this realisation, the observed value of $X(2, 4)$ is 4, and the observed value of $X(0, 4)$ is 7. By convention, the random variable $X(0, t)$ is usually written simply as $X(t)$.

Activity 3.3 Notation

For the realisation of the continuous-time process in Figure 3.4, write down the values of $X(1, 3)$, $X(4, 5)$, $X(0, 2)$, $X(1)$ and $X(3)$.

For a Poisson process with rate λ, the number of events that occur during *any* interval of length t (denoted $N(t)$ in Subsection 3.1) has a Poisson distribution with parameter λt. So, in particular, $X(0, t) = X(t) \sim \text{Poisson}(\lambda t)$. Also, since $X(t_1, t_2)$ is the number of events that occur in the interval $(t_1, t_2]$, which has length $t_2 - t_1$, it has a Poisson distribution with parameter $\lambda(t_2 - t_1)$; that is, $X(t_1, t_2) \sim \text{Poisson}(\lambda(t_2 - t_1))$. Although for a Poisson process this distribution depends only on the length of the interval, note that for many continuous-time processes, the distribution of $X(t_1, t_2)$ depends on the values of both t_1 and t_2. You will meet a process for which this is the case in Section 6.

Waiting times

The waiting time from the start of observation to the first event in any continuous-time process is conventionally denoted T_1, and the waiting time between the first event and the second is denoted T_2. In general, the waiting time between the $(n-1)$th event and the nth event is denoted T_n. The waiting time from the start of observation to the time of the nth event is denoted W_n: $W_n = T_1 + T_2 + \cdots + T_n$.

This notation is illustrated in Figure 3.5.

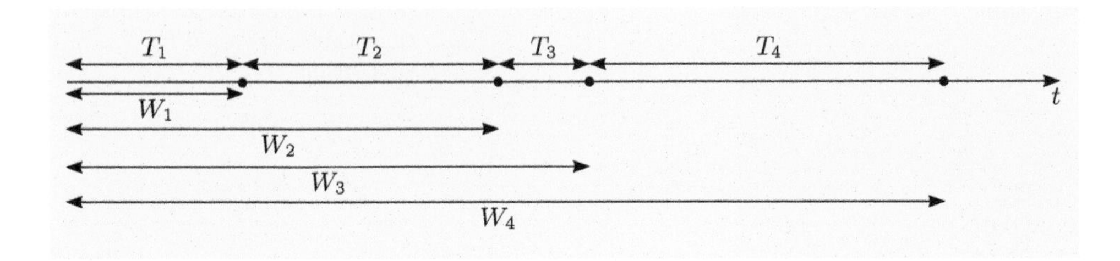

Figure 3.5 Waiting times

For a Poisson process, the random variables $T_1, T_2, \ldots, T_n$ are independent identically distributed exponential random variables with parameter λ.

Activity 3.4 The distribution of W_n

Write down the distribution of W_n, the waiting time from the start of observation to the nth event in a Poisson process with rate λ.

The notation introduced in this subsection, which will be used on many occasions in M343, is summarised in the following box.

Notation for continuous-time processes

- ◇ $X(t_1, t_2)$ is the number of events that occur in the interval $(t_1, t_2]$.
- ◇ $X(t) = X(0, t)$ is the number of events that occur in the interval $(0, t]$.
- ◇ T_1 is the time at which the first event occurs.
- ◇ T_n is the waiting time between the $(n-1)$th event and the nth event.
- ◇ W_n is the time at which the nth event occurs.

3.3 Simulation

The simplest way to simulate the occurrences of events in a Poisson process is to simulate the sequence of waiting times between events. These are independent observations of the random variable $T \sim M(\lambda)$, where λ is the rate of occurrence.

A table of random numbers from the exponential distribution with mean 1 is provided in the *Handbook*. To obtain a sequence of random numbers $t_1, t_2, \ldots$ from the exponential distribution $M(\lambda)$ (which has mean $1/\lambda$), each term in a sequence of random numbers $e_1, e_2, \ldots$ from the table must be multiplied by the mean $1/\lambda$:

Random numbers from $M(1)$ are provided in Table 6 in the *Handbook*.

$$t_j = \frac{1}{\lambda} e_j, \quad j = 1, 2, \ldots .$$

Example 3.3 Simulating events in a Poisson process

Suppose that events in a Poisson process occur at the rate of one every 10 minutes, so that the rate λ is $1/10$ per minute, and hence the mean time between events is $1/\lambda = 10$ minutes.

To simulate the sequence of events occurring in the Poisson process, random numbers from $M(1)$ must be multiplied by 10 to obtain the times between successive events in minutes. The details of a simulation of the events from the start of observation for one hour are set out in Table 3.3. The random numbers are taken from the eleventh row of Table 6 in the *Handbook*.

In practice, computers rather than tables are used for simulation.

Table 3.3 A simulation

n	e_n	$t_n = 10e_n$	$w_n = t_1 + \cdots + t_n$
1	0.2316	2.316	$2.316 \simeq 2.32$
2	1.8293	18.293	$20.609 \simeq 20.61$
3	1.1956	11.956	$32.565 \simeq 32.57$
4	3.2992	32.992	$65.557 \simeq 65.56$

The first event occurs after $t_1 \simeq 2.32$ minutes. The time at which the second event occurs is given by $w_2 = t_1 + t_2 \simeq 20.61$ minutes, and the third event occurs at $w_3 = t_1 + t_2 + t_3 \simeq 32.57$ minutes.

The time of the fourth event is $w_4 \simeq 65.56$ minutes, which is more than one hour after the start of observation. So three events occur in the first hour of observation, and the times in minutes at which the first three events occur are

$$w_1 = 2.32, \quad w_2 = 20.61, \quad w_3 = 32.57. \quad \blacklozenge$$

Activity 3.5 Computer failures

In an investigation into computer reliability, a particular unit failed on average every 652 seconds. Assuming that the incidence of failures may be adequately modelled by a Poisson process, use the tenth row of Table 6 in the *Handbook* to simulate one hour's usage after switching the unit on. Give the times of failures to the nearest second.

Musa, J.D., Iannino, A. and Okumoto, K. (1987) *Software Reliability: Measurement, Prediction, Application*, McGraw-Hill.

Summary of Section 3

In this section, the Poisson process has been described. This is the continuous-time analogue of the Bernoulli process. It is a model for events that occur at random in continuous time at a constant rate.

If the rate of occurrence of events is λ, then the number of events that occur in an interval of length t has a Poisson distribution with parameter λt, and the waiting time between successive events has an exponential distribution with parameter λ. You have learned how to simulate the occurrences of events in a Poisson process using random observations from the exponential distribution with mean 1.

Notation has been introduced for the number of events in an interval, for the times between events, and for the times at which events occur. The notation applies to *any* continuous-time process.

Exercises on Section 3

Exercise 3.1 A Poisson process

Events occur according to a Poisson process in time with, on average, sixteen minutes between events.

(a) Write down the probability distribution of the waiting time T between events, where T is measured in hours.

(b) Write down the probability distribution of the number of events in any hour-long interval.

(c) If there were seven events between 2 pm and 3 pm yesterday, calculate the probability that there was at most one event between 3 pm and 4 pm.

(d) Calculate the probability that the waiting time between successive events will exceed half an hour.

Exercise 3.2 Volcanic eruptions

Data collected on major volcanic eruptions in the northern hemisphere give a mean time between eruptions of 29 months. Assume that such eruptions occur as a Poisson process in time.

(a) Calculate the expected number of eruptions during a five-year period.

(b) Calculate the probability that there are exactly two eruptions during a five-year period.

(c) Calculate the probability that at least three years pass after you have read this exercise before the next eruption.

Exercise 3.3 Light bulb failures

In Subsection 3.1, it is suggested that light bulb failures in the home might reasonably be modelled as a Poisson process with a rate of one failure every three months.

(a) Use this model to simulate the incidence of failures during a two-year period, setting out your realisation in a table similar to Table 3.3. Use random numbers e_n from the twelfth row of Table 6 in the *Handbook*.

(b) How many failures were there in your simulation? From which probability distribution is this number an observation?

4 A more formal approach to the Poisson process

In Subsection 3.1, the distribution of the number of events in a Poisson process that occur in an interval of length t, and the distribution of the time between successive events, were stated without proof. In order to derive these results, a more formal approach to the Poisson process is required than has been adopted so far. In this section, the assumptions of a Poisson process are expressed mathematically as three *postulates*. The postulates are then used to derive these results. Although you will not be expected to reproduce the derivations, you should work through this section thoroughly and make sure that you understand the ideas that are introduced here. The approach used here is used again in *Book 4*.

The first two postulates of the Poisson process express mathematically the assumptions that events occur singly and that the rate of occurrence of events remains constant. These postulates state the probability of one event in a short interval and the probability of two or more events in a short interval. The length of this short interval is denoted by δt (read as 'delta t').

The first postulate states that the probability that one event occurs in any interval of length δt is approximately $\lambda\,\delta t$. The fact that this probability is the same for any interval of length δt implies that the rate λ at which events occur remains constant over time. This postulate is written more precisely as follows.

I The probability that (exactly) one event occurs in any small time interval $[t, t + \delta t]$ is equal to $\lambda\,\delta t + o(\delta t)$.

The notation $o(\delta t)$ (read as 'little-oh of δt') is used to represent any function of δt that is of 'smaller order' than δt. Formally, we can write $f(\delta t) = o(\delta t)$ for any function f of δt such that

$$\frac{f(\delta t)}{\delta t} \to 0 \quad \text{as } \delta t \to 0. \tag{4.1}$$

For example, $(\delta t)^2 = o(\delta t)$ since

$$\frac{(\delta t)^2}{\delta t} = \delta t \to 0 \quad \text{as } \delta t \to 0,$$

and $(\delta t)^3 = o(\delta t)$ since

$$\frac{(\delta t)^3}{\delta t} = (\delta t)^2 \to 0 \quad \text{as } \delta t \to 0.$$

Since the notation $o(\delta t)$ is used to represent any function of δt that satisfies (4.1), it follows that

$$\frac{o(\delta t)}{\delta t} \to 0 \quad \text{as } \delta t \to 0.$$

The second postulate states formally the probability that two or more events occur in a short interval of length δt. It is written as follows.

II The probability that two or more events occur in any small time interval $[t, t + \delta t]$ is equal to $o(\delta t)$.

Essentially, this postulate expresses mathematically the assumption that events occur singly in a Poisson process.

The third postulate is a formal statement of the third assumption made in Subsection 3.1.

III The occurrence of events after any time t is independent of the occurrence of events before time t.

These three postulates are summarised in the following box.

Postulates for the Poisson process

A Poisson process is specified by three postulates.

I The probability that (exactly) one event occurs in any small time interval $[t, t + \delta t]$ is equal to $\lambda\,\delta t + o(\delta t)$.

II The probability that two or more events occur in any small time interval $[t, t + \delta t]$ is equal to $o(\delta t)$.

III The occurrence of events after any time t is independent of the occurrence of events before time t.

The distribution of $X(t)$

One sequence of random variables associated with a Poisson process is $\{X(t); t \geq 0\}$, where $X(t)$ denotes the number of events that have occurred by time t. It is assumed here that the process starts at time 0, so $X(0) = 0$. The distribution of $X(t)$ is given by $X(t) \sim \text{Poisson}(\lambda t)$, which may be proved formally as follows.

Suppose that observation of a Poisson process starts at time 0 and continues for a fixed time t. The number of events that occur in the interval $[0, t]$ is a random variable $X(t)$. The probability mass function of $X(t)$ will be denoted $p_x(t)$, so

$$p_x(t) = P(X(t) = x).$$

This is not the standard notation for a p.m.f. It is adopted here to stress that the probability is a function of t as well as of x.

The probability $p_0(t) = P(X(t) = 0)$ will be found first. This is the probability that no event occurs in $[0, t]$. The interval $[0, t]$ and a further short interval $[t, t + \delta t]$ will be considered, and $p_0(t + \delta t)$, the probability that no event has occurred at the end of the second interval, will be derived. Using Postulate III, the occurrence of events after any time t is independent of what happened before time t, so

$$\begin{aligned} p_0(t + \delta t) &= P(\text{no event by time } t + \delta t) \\ &= P(\text{no event in } [0, t]) \times P(\text{no event in } [t, t + \delta t]). \end{aligned}$$

The first of these two probabilities is $p_0(t)$. The second probability is equal to

$$\begin{aligned} &1 - P(\text{one event in } [t, t + \delta t]) - P(\text{two or more events in } [t, t + \delta t]) \\ &= 1 - (\lambda\,\delta t + o(\delta t)) - o(\delta t), \quad \text{using Postulates I and II,} \\ &= 1 - \lambda\,\delta t + o(\delta t). \end{aligned}$$

This illustrates one of the advantages of the notation $o(\delta t)$: expressions involving $o(\delta t)$ can be simplified. Above, $-o(\delta t) - o(\delta t)$ could be replaced by $o(\delta t)$ because adding or subtracting any finite number of functions of order smaller than δt always gives a function of order smaller than δt. Thus

$$p_0(t + \delta t) = p_0(t) \times (1 - \lambda\,\delta t + o(\delta t)),$$

which can be written

$$\frac{p_0(t + \delta t) - p_0(t)}{\delta t} = -\lambda\, p_0(t) + \frac{o(\delta t)}{\delta t}.$$

Since $p_0(t) \leq 1$, $o(\delta t)\, p_0(t) = o(\delta t)$.

Now let δt tend to 0. The left-hand side tends *by definition* to the derivative of $p_0(t)$ with respect to t. On the right-hand side, $o(\delta t)/\delta t$ tends to 0 by definition. This leads to the differential equation

$$\frac{dp_0(t)}{dt} = -\lambda\, p_0(t). \tag{4.2}$$

This equation can be integrated using separation of variables:

The separation of variables method is described in *Book 1* and in the *Handbook*.

$$\int \frac{dp_0(t)}{p_0(t)} = \int -\lambda\, dt.$$

Performing both integrations gives

$$\log p_0(t) = -\lambda t + c. \tag{4.3}$$

When $t = 0$, observation of the process is just starting, so no event has occurred, and hence

$$p_0(0) = P(\text{no event in } [0, 0]) = 1.$$

Putting $t = 0$ in (4.3) gives

$$\log 1 = 0 + c,$$

so $c = 0$. Thus the solution is

$$\log p_0(t) = -\lambda t,$$

which gives

$$p_0(t) = e^{-\lambda t}. \tag{4.4}$$

The differential equations satisfied by $p_x(t)$ $(x = 1, 2, \ldots)$ are derived in a similar way to the differential equation for $p_0(t)$. For example,

$$\begin{aligned} p_1(t+\delta t) &= P(\text{one event has occurred by time } t+\delta t) \\ &= P([\text{one event in } [0,t] \text{ and no event in } [t,t+\delta t]\,] \\ &\qquad \cup [\text{no event in } [0,t] \text{ and one event in } [t,t+\delta t]\,]). \end{aligned}$$

This is the union of two mutually exclusive events, so their separate probabilities can be added:

$$\begin{aligned} p_1(t+\delta t) &= P([\text{one event in } [0,t]\,] \cap [\text{no event in } [t,t+\delta t]\,]) \\ &\quad + P([\text{no event in } [0,t]\,] \cap [\text{one event in } [t,t+\delta t]\,]). \end{aligned}$$

Using the postulates gives

$$p_1(t+\delta t) = p_1(t) \times (1 - \lambda\,\delta t + o(\delta t)) + p_0(t) \times (\lambda\,\delta t + o(\delta t)).$$

Rearranging this equation gives

$$\frac{p_1(t+\delta t) - p_1(t)}{\delta t} = \lambda(p_0(t) - p_1(t)) + \frac{o(\delta t)}{\delta t}.$$

Letting $\delta t \to 0$ leads to the differential equation

$$\frac{dp_1(t)}{dt} = \lambda\,p_0(t) - \lambda\,p_1(t). \qquad (4.5)$$

Substituting for $p_0(t)$ using (4.4), this becomes

$$\frac{dp_1(t)}{dt} + \lambda\,p_1(t) = \lambda e^{-\lambda t}.$$

This differential equation can be solved using the integrating factor method. In this case, the integrating factor is $e^{\lambda t}$, so both sides are multiplied by $e^{\lambda t}$:

The integrating factor method is described in *Book 1* and in the *Handbook*.

$$e^{\lambda t}\,\frac{dp_1(t)}{dt} + \lambda e^{\lambda t}\,p_1(t) = \lambda.$$

The left-hand side is the derivative of the product $e^{\lambda t} \times p_1(t)$, so the differential equation can be rewritten as

$$\frac{d}{dt}(e^{\lambda t}\,p_1(t)) = \lambda.$$

Integrating this equation gives

$$e^{\lambda t}\,p_1(t) = \lambda t + c.$$

When $t = 0$, no event has occurred, so $p_1(0) = P(X(0) = 1) = 0$, and hence $c = 0$. Therefore

$$p_1(t) = \lambda t e^{-\lambda t}.$$

For $x = 2, 3, \ldots$,

$$\begin{aligned} p_x(t+\delta t) &= P(x \text{ events have occurred by time } t+\delta t) \\ &= P([x \text{ events in } [0,t] \text{ and no event in } [t,t+\delta t]\,] \\ &\qquad \cup [(x-1) \text{ events in } [0,t] \text{ and one event in } [t,t+\delta t]\,] \\ &\qquad \cup [(x-2) \text{ events in } [0,t] \text{ and two events in } [t,t+\delta t]\,] \\ &\qquad \cup \ \ldots \\ &\qquad \cup [\text{no event in } [0,t] \text{ and } x \text{ events in } [t,t+\delta t]\,]). \end{aligned}$$

This is the union of mutually exclusive events, so their separate probabilities can be added:

$$\begin{aligned} p_x(t+\delta t) &= P([x \text{ events in } [0,t]\,] \cap [\text{no event in } [t,t+\delta t]\,]) \\ &\quad + P([(x-1) \text{ events in } [0,t]\,] \cap [\text{one event in } [t,t,+\delta t]\,]) \\ &\quad + P([(x-2) \text{ events in } [0,t]\,] \cap [\text{two events in } [t,t+\delta t]\,]) \\ &\quad + \cdots + P([\text{no event in } [0,t]\,] \cap [x \text{ events in } [t,t+\delta t]\,]). \end{aligned}$$

Using the postulates gives

$$\begin{aligned} p_x(t+\delta t) &= p_x(t) \times (1 - \lambda\,\delta t + o(\delta t)) + p_{x-1}(t) \times (\lambda\,\delta t + o(\delta t)) + o(\delta t) \\ &= p_x(t) + \lambda(p_{x-1}(t) - p_x(t))\,\delta t + o(\delta t). \end{aligned}$$

Again, the brevity of the interval $[t, t+\delta t]$ has been used to attach probabilities to the possibilities that nothing happens, one thing happens, or more than one thing happens.

Rearranging this equation gives

$$\frac{p_x(t+\delta t) - p_x(t)}{\delta t} = \lambda(p_{x-1}(t) - p_x(t)) + \frac{o(\delta t)}{\delta t}.$$

Letting $\delta t \to 0$ leads to the differential equations

$$\frac{dp_x(t)}{dt} = \lambda(p_{x-1}(t) - p_x(t)), \quad x = 2, 3, \ldots. \tag{4.6}$$

Note that the differential equation (4.5) for $p_1(t)$ is of this form with $x = 1$.

A set of differential equations satisfied by the p.m.f.s $p_x(t)$ has been derived. Each equation contains both $p_x(t)$ and $p_{x-1}(t)$. The equations can be solved recursively.

Activity 4.1 Finding $p_2(t)$

Using the value of $p_1(t)$, the differential equation in (4.6) for $x = 2$ can be solved using the method that was used for $x = 1$. Solve this differential equation to derive an expression for $p_2(t)$.

Continuing in this way, $p_3(t)$ could be found, then $p_4(t)$, and so on. However, if you look at the results so far, you may recognise that $p_0(t)$, $p_1(t)$ and $p_2(t)$ are probabilities from a Poisson distribution. The p.m.f. of the Poisson distribution with parameter μ is

$$p_X(x) = P(X = x) = \frac{e^{-\mu}\mu^x}{x!}, \quad x = 0, 1, 2, \ldots.$$

Hence $p_0(t)$, $p_1(t)$ and $p_2(t)$ are the first three probabilities in a Poisson distribution with parameter λt. That $X(t)$ has a Poisson distribution with parameter λt can be either proved by induction or verified by substitution in the general differential equation. The second of these methods will be used.

If $p_x(t) = e^{-\lambda t}(\lambda t)^x/x!$, then

$$\begin{aligned} \frac{d}{dt}(p_x(t)) &= \frac{-\lambda e^{-\lambda t}(\lambda t)^x}{x!} + \frac{e^{-\lambda t}\lambda^x x t^{x-1}}{x!} \\ &= -\lambda\,p_x(t) + \frac{e^{-\lambda t}(\lambda t)^{x-1}\lambda}{(x-1)!} \\ &= -\lambda\,p_x(t) + \lambda\,p_{x-1}(t). \end{aligned}$$

This is the differential equation (4.6). Therefore the solution of the set of differential equations (4.6) with initial values $p_0(0) = 1$, $p_x(0) = 0$, for $x = 1, 2, \ldots$, is the p.m.f. of the Poisson distribution with parameter λt.

The distribution of $X(t)$

The number of events that occur by time t in a Poisson process is a random variable $X(t)$. In a Poisson process with rate λ, $X(t)$ has a Poisson distribution with parameter λt. That is, $X(t) \sim \text{Poisson}(\lambda t)$ and

$$p_x(t) = P(X(t) = x) = \frac{e^{-\lambda t}(\lambda t)^x}{x!}, \quad x = 0, 1, \ldots.$$

Since λ, the rate of occurrence of events, is constant, this result holds for any time interval of length t; it does not matter when observation of the process starts.

Waiting times

The other quantity that is often of interest in a Poisson process, and indeed in many random processes, is the time between successive events. You have seen that the time from the start of the process until the first event is denoted T_1, and the time between the $(n-1)$th event and the nth event is denoted T_n. Each T_n is referred to as an **inter-event time**.

The distribution of T_1 can be derived using the distribution of $X(t)$. Since T_1 exceeds t if and only if no event occurs in $[0, t]$,

$$\begin{aligned} P(T_1 > t) &= P(\text{no event occurs in } [0,t]) \\ &= P(X(t) = 0) \\ &= e^{-\lambda t}, \quad \text{since } X(t) \sim \text{Poisson}(\lambda t). \end{aligned}$$

If T_1 has c.d.f. $F(t)$, then

$$F(t) = P(T_1 \leq t) = 1 - P(T_1 > t),$$

so

$$F(t) = 1 - e^{-\lambda t}, \quad t \geq 0.$$

Hence T_1 has the exponential distribution with parameter λ: $T_1 \sim M(\lambda)$.

By the memoryless property of the exponential distribution, observation can start at any stage of the process: the time at which the previous event occurred is irrelevant. Whether it occurred immediately before observation started or a long time before, the time until the next event always has an exponential distribution. Also, for $n = 1, 2, \ldots$, the distribution of the inter-event time T_n is exponential with parameter λ.

The distribution of T_n

In a Poisson process with rate λ, T_1, the time from the start of observation to the first event, has an exponential distribution with parameter λ.

For $n = 2, 3, \ldots$, T_n, the time between the $(n-1)$th event and the nth event, has an exponential distribution with parameter λ.

That is,

$$T_n \sim M(\lambda), \quad n = 1, 2, \ldots .$$

This result provides the simplest method of simulating observations from a Poisson process. Independent observations from $M(\lambda)$ can be used to simulate the inter-event times.

This result was used in Example 3.3.

Many of the processes studied in M343 are extensions of the Poisson process. Several models for events occurring in time, obtained by modifying the postulates in various ways, are discussed in Sections 5 to 7. The Poisson process also provides the basis for many of the models discussed in *Book 4*.

Summary of Section 4

In this section, the assumptions of a Poisson process have been expressed mathematically as postulates, and the postulates have been used to derive the distributions of $X(t)$, the number of events that occur by time t, and T_1, the time at which the first event occurs.

5 *The multivariate Poisson process*

A **multivariate Poisson process** is a Poisson process in which each event may be just one of several different types of event. For instance, in traffic research, an event may correspond to the passage of a vehicle past a point of observation by the side of a road. The vehicles may themselves be classified as private cars, lorries, buses, motorcycles, and so on. So there are several types of event, and each event in the process is of just one type.

A typical realisation of a multivariate Poisson process is shown in Figure 5.1.

Figure 5.1 Events in a multivariate Poisson process

In general, the multivariate Poisson process may be described as follows.

Multivariate Poisson process

Suppose that events occur as a Poisson process in time at rate λ, and that each event is one of k types. If the probability that an event is of type i is p_i, where $p_1 + \cdots + p_k = 1$, and occurrences of events of different types are independent of each other, then the process is a **multivariate Poisson process.**

Consider the occurrence of events of type i in the small interval $[t, t+\delta t]$:

$$\begin{aligned}
&P(\text{one event of type } i \text{ occurs in } [t, t+\delta t]) \\
&= P(\text{one event occurs in } [t, t+\delta t] \text{ and it is of type } i) \\
&\quad + P(\text{more than one event in } [t, t+\delta t] \text{ and one of them is of type } i) \\
&= P(\text{one event in } [t, t+\delta t]) \times P(\text{an event is of type } i) + o(\delta t) \\
&= (\lambda\, \delta t + o(\delta t)) \times p_i + o(\delta t) \\
&= \lambda p_i\, \delta t + o(\delta t).
\end{aligned}$$

So

$$P(\text{one event of type } i \text{ occurs in } [t, t+\delta t]) = \lambda p_i\, \delta t + o(\delta t).$$

This is Postulate I for a Poisson process with rate λp_i. The other two postulates are also satisfied by the process of events of type i. Therefore events of type i occur as in a Poisson process with rate λp_i.

It follows that the multivariate Poisson process is built up of k independent Poisson processes with rates $\lambda p_1, \ldots, \lambda p_k$. This result can be used to calculate probabilities associated with events of different types.

Example 5.1 Vehicles passing an observer

Vehicles pass an observer standing at the edge of a main road according to a Poisson process at the rate of 100 vehicles per hour. Of these vehicles, the proportions of vehicles that are cars, lorries, coaches and motorcycles are 0.6, 0.3, 0.08 and 0.02, respectively.

What is the probability that more than four lorries pass the observer in a ten-minute interval? And what is the average waiting time between successive motorcycles passing the observer?

The process of vehicles passing the observer is a multivariate Poisson process: the proportions of the four types of vehicle are $p_1 = 0.6$, $p_2 = 0.3$, $p_3 = 0.08$ and $p_4 = 0.02$. Since $\lambda = 100$ per hour, the rates at which vehicles of the different types pass the observer are

$$\lambda_1 = \lambda p_1 = 60 \text{ per hour}, \quad \lambda_2 = \lambda p_2 = 30 \text{ per hour},$$
$$\lambda_3 = \lambda p_3 = 8 \text{ per hour}, \quad \lambda_4 = \lambda p_4 = 2 \text{ per hour}.$$

Thus, for example, lorries pass the observer at the rate $\lambda_2 = 30$ per hour.

If the number of lorries that pass the observer in t hours is denoted $L(t)$, then the number of lorries that pass the observer in ten minutes ($\frac{1}{6}$ hour) is $L(\frac{1}{6})$. This has a Poisson distribution with parameter $\lambda_2 t = 30/6 = 5$, so the probability that more than four lorries pass the observer in ten minutes is $P(L(\frac{1}{6}) > 4)$, where $L(\frac{1}{6}) \sim \text{Poisson}(5)$. That is,

$$\begin{aligned} P(L(\tfrac{1}{6}) > 4) &= 1 - P(L(\tfrac{1}{6}) \leq 4) \\ &= 1 - e^{-5}\left(1 + 5 + \frac{5^2}{2!} + \frac{5^3}{3!} + \frac{5^4}{4!}\right) \\ &\simeq 0.5595. \end{aligned}$$

Now consider the waiting time between successive motorcycles. This has an exponential distribution with parameter $\lambda_4 = 2$. So the mean waiting time between successive motorcycles is

$$\frac{1}{\lambda_4} = \tfrac{1}{2} \text{ hour} = 30 \text{ minutes.} \quad \blacklozenge$$

Activity 5.1 Bank customers

Customers arrive at a bank according to a Poisson process at the rate of ten per minute. The proportion of customers who simply wish to draw out money from a cashpoint machine (type A) is 0.6, the proportion who wish to pay in money (type B) is 0.3, and the proportion who wish to carry out a more complicated transaction at the counter (type C) is 0.1.

(a) Calculate the probability that more than five customers arrive in an interval of length 30 seconds.

(b) Calculate the probability that six customers of type A arrive in one minute.

(c) Calculate the probability that six customers of type A, three of type B and at least one of type C arrive in one minute.

A multivariate Poisson process can alternatively be described as follows.

Suppose that events of type 1 occur as a Poisson process in time at rate λ_1, events of type 2 occur as a Poisson process in time at rate λ_2, ..., and events of type k occur as a Poisson process in time at rate λ_k. If the Poisson processes may be assumed to be developing independently of one another, then the sequence of events obtained by superposing the events from the processes on the same time axis occurs as a Poisson process with rate

$$\lambda = \lambda_1 + \lambda_2 + \cdots + \lambda_k.$$

In any realisation of this process, the probability that an event is of type i is given by

$$p_i = \frac{\lambda_i}{\lambda} = \frac{\lambda_i}{\lambda_1 + \lambda_2 + \cdots + \lambda_k}.$$

You will need to use this result in Activity 5.2.

Activity 5.2 Telephone calls

A university tutor has noticed that over the course of an evening, telephone calls arrive from students according to a Poisson process at the rate of one every 90 minutes. Independently, calls arrive from members of her family according to a Poisson process at the rate of one every three hours, and calls from friends arrive according to a Poisson process at the rate of one call per hour. She does not receive any other calls.

(a) Calculate the probability that between 7 pm and 9 pm tomorrow evening, the tutor's telephone will not ring.

(b) Calculate the probability that the first call after 9 pm is from a student.

(c) Given that she receives four telephone calls one evening, calculate the probability that exactly two of the calls are from members of her family.

Summary of Section 5

The multivariate Poisson process is a model for events occurring at random in time in which each event may be one of several types. You have seen that it can also be thought of as the process obtained when the events in several independent Poisson processes are superposed on the same time axis.

Exercises on Section 5

Exercise 5.1 Post office customers

Customers arrive at a small post office according to a Poisson process at the rate of eight customers an hour. In general, 70% of customers post letters, 5% post parcels and the remaining 25% make purchases unrelated to the postal service.

(a) At what rate do customers arrive at the post office to post parcels?

(b) Calculate the probability that the interval between successive customers arriving to post parcels is greater than an hour.

(c) Calculate the probability that over a three-hour period, fewer than five customers arrive to post letters.

(d) Calculate the median waiting time between customers arriving to post something (either a letter or a parcel).

Exercise 5.2 Library acquisitions

New acquisitions arrive independently at a local library as follows: new works of fiction according to a Poisson process at the rate of eight a week, biographies according to a Poisson process with rate one a week, works of reference according to a Poisson process at the rate of one every four weeks, and non-text items according to a Poisson process at the rate of five a week. Assume that the library operates for seven days a week.

(a) Calculate the probability that at least two non-text acquisitions will arrive next week.

(b) Calculate the probability that no new work of fiction will arrive tomorrow.

(c) On average, what proportions of new acquisitions are fiction, biography, reference and non-text?

6 The non-homogeneous Poisson process

The Poisson process is a model for events occurring at random in continuous time at a constant rate λ. In Subsection 6.1, several examples are described of situations where the rate at which events occur cannot reasonably be assumed to be constant, and a model for such events is introduced. This model is the non-homogeneous Poisson process. The work in Subsection 6.1 includes a chapter of the computer book. Some basic results for the non-homogeneous Poisson process are derived in Subsection 6.2, and simulation is discussed in Subsection 6.3.

6.1 The model

Examples are used in this subsection to motivate and introduce a model for events occurring at random in time at a rate that changes with time.

Example 6.1 Mining accidents

Data are available on the dates of accidents in coal mines that were due to explosions and in which there were ten or more fatalities. Figure 6.1 shows the cumulative number of such explosions in coal mines in Great Britain for the period 15 March 1851 to 22 March 1962.

Jarrett, R.G. (1979) 'A note on intervals between coal-mining disasters', *Biometrika*, vol. 66, no. 1, pp. 191–3.

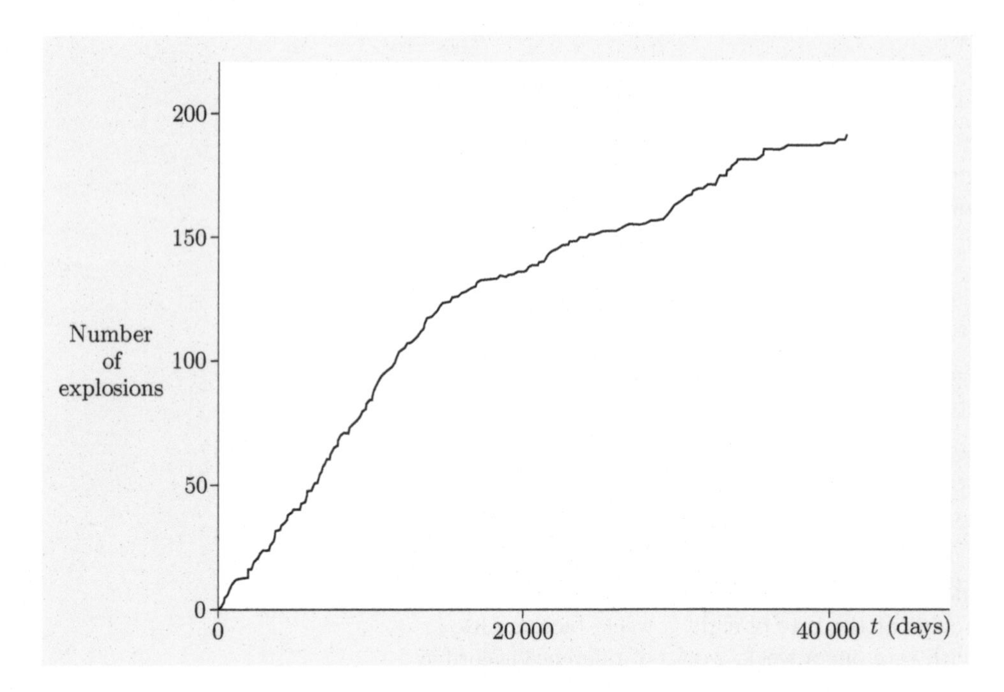

Figure 6.1 Cumulative number of explosions in coal mines in Great Britain, in which ten or more miners were killed, against time

This graph is roughly linear for the first 14 000 days (up to about 1890), but the gradient then becomes less steep. This means that the rate of occurrence of accidents decreased. A possible explanation for this is that safety precautions in coal mines were improved in about 1890. This is an example of a process where the rate of occurrence of events is not constant, but changes with time. ♦

Example 6.2 *Road accidents*

Another example of an event in time is a fatality in a road accident. The number of such fatalities in Great Britain in each year from 1992 to 2008 is shown in Figure 6.2.

These data were obtained from the website www.statistics.gov.uk/STATBASE in January 2010.

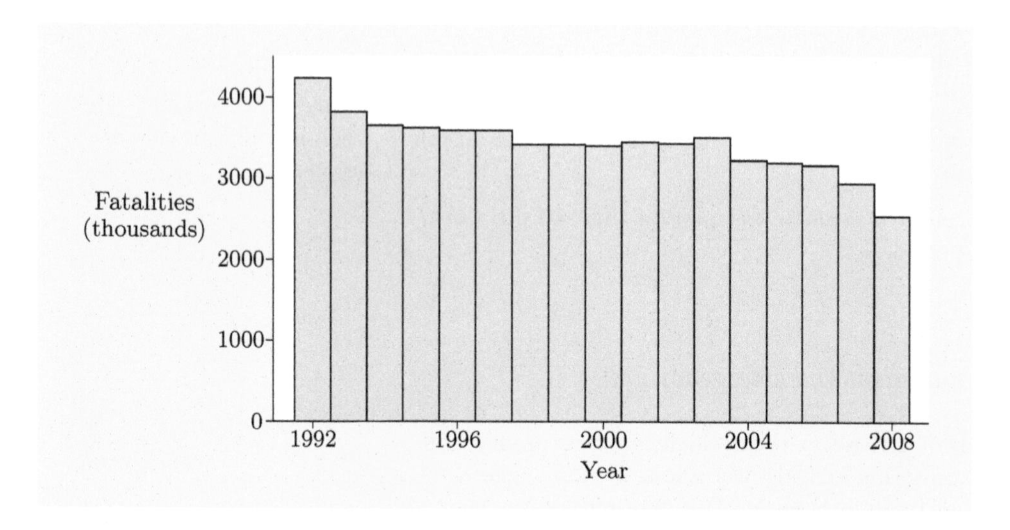

Figure 6.2 Fatalities in road accidents in Great Britain from 1992 to 2008

Figure 6.2 shows that over the period the annual number of deaths from road accidents tended to decline. As with coal-mining disasters, the rate of occurrence of events appears to alter with time. ♦

Example 6.3 *Mistakes during learning*

In any learning situation (such as a child learning to ride a bicycle, or an adult learning to perform some complex task, such as text-processing or bricklaying) there will be an initial period during which many accidents will happen and mistakes will be made. Then, as the learner becomes more proficient, mistakes still occur haphazardly – that is, at random – but at a rate that is lower than in the initial stages. Figure 6.3 shows a possible realisation of events, their incidence becoming sparser with passing time. (But notice that there is no regular pattern to the events: it is in the nature of accidents and mistakes that they are unexpected and unforecastable.)

Figure 6.3 Realisation of a random process: mistakes during learning ♦

Example 6.4 *Learning to ride*

A young girl learning to ride a bicycle has accidents at random. However, as she improves, the rate at which she has accidents decreases, so the Poisson process does not provide an adequate model. A model is needed in which the rate decreases with time.

One possibility is to modify the Poisson process by changing the first postulate, which states that the probability that one event occurs in $[t, t + \delta t]$ is $\lambda\, \delta t + o(\delta t)$. Suppose that the probability that an accident occurs in the interval $[t, t + \delta t]$ is $[24/(2 + t)]\, \delta t + o(\delta t)$, where t is measured in days. The accident rate $24/(2 + t)$ decreases with time: when the girl starts to learn ($t = 0$) she has an accident once every two hours on average, but after ten days ($t = 10$) the rate has dropped to two a day, and after a year it is only about one a fortnight.

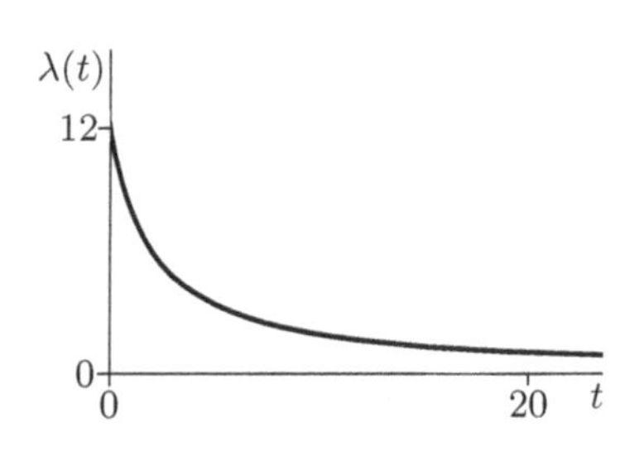

Figure 6.4 Accident rate when learning to ride a bicycle

The second and third postulates remain unchanged: accidents occur independently of each other, and the rate at time t is independent of how many accidents the girl has had before time t.

If $\lambda(t)$ denotes the accident rate at time t, then $\lambda(t) = 24/(2 + t)$, $t \geq 0$. A graph of $\lambda(t)$ against t is shown in Figure 6.4.

Note that this model makes the rather unrealistic assumption that the girl does nothing else during the learning period. ♦

Activity 6.1 Arrivals at an accident and emergency unit

Suppose that a model is required for arrivals at the accident and emergency unit in a hospital. Experience from monitoring arrivals over a long period suggests that there is a daily cycle, and that the unit is busier at some times of day than at others, so a Poisson process is not an adequate model for arrivals. In fact, arrivals may be regarded as occurring at a roughly constant rate from (say) 6 am to 6 pm, but the rate starts to rise after 6 pm until 2 am, after which arrivals are rather sparse until 6 am.

Suppose that $\lambda(t)$ denotes the arrival rate at time t. Draw a rough sketch showing what a graph of $\lambda(t)$ against t might look like over a 24-hour period.

The **non-homogeneous Poisson process**, in which the rate changes with time, is defined by three postulates. As has already been suggested, the second and third postulates are the same as for the Poisson process. The first postulate is a modification of the first postulate of the Poisson process that allows the rate of occurrence of events to vary with time.

I The probability that (exactly) one event occurs in the small time interval $[t, t + \delta t]$ is equal to $\lambda(t)\, \delta t + o(\delta t)$.

The function $\lambda(t)$ can take any form – for example, linear, quadratic or trigonometric – provided that $\lambda(t) > 0$. The behaviour of a non-homogeneous Poisson process can be illustrated by running simulations for several different functions $\lambda(t)$. This is most easily done on a computer. The rest of this subsection consists of working through a chapter of the computer book.

Refer to Chapter 1 of the computer book for the rest of the work in this subsection.

6.2 Basic results

In this subsection, the distributions of the number of events in an interval and the times at which successive events occur in a non-homogeneous Poisson process are discussed. The derivations of these results are similar to those of the corresponding results for a Poisson process that were given in Section 4.

The number of events in an interval

For a non-homogeneous Poisson process, $\lambda(t)$, the rate at which events occur, changes with time, so the distribution of $X(t_1, t_2)$, the number of events in the interval $(t_1, t_2]$, depends on t_1 as well as on the length of the interval.

First consider the interval $(0, t]$. The number of events in $(0, t]$ is denoted $X(0, t)$, or simply $X(t)$. The distribution of $X(t)$ can be derived by modifying the argument used in Section 4 for a Poisson process. The details are very similar, and you will not be expected to derive the result, so they will be omitted. The result is stated in the following box.

The distribution of $X(t)$

If $X(t)$ is the number of events that occur in a non-homogeneous Poisson process with rate $\lambda(t)$ during the interval $(0, t]$, then $X(t)$ has a Poisson distribution with parameter $\mu(t)$,

$$X(t) \sim \text{Poisson}(\mu(t)), \qquad (6.1)$$

where

$$\mu(t) = \int_0^t \lambda(u)\, du. \qquad (6.2)$$

The mean of a Poisson distribution is equal to its parameter, so the expected number of events in the interval $(0, t]$ is

$$E[X(t)] = \mu(t).$$

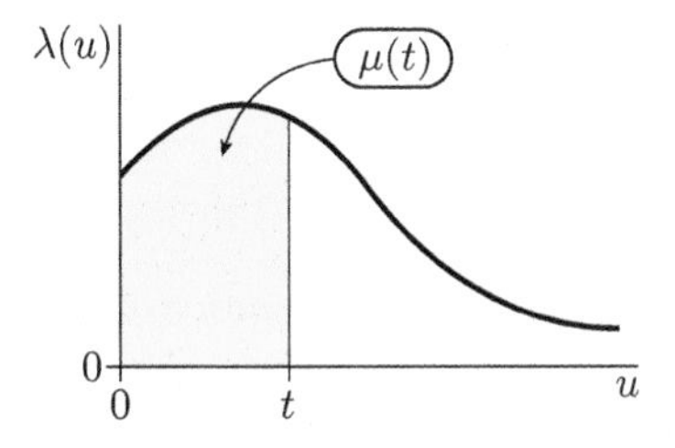

Figure 6.5 The expected number of events in the interval $(0, t]$

Since $\mu(t)$ is found by integrating the rate $\lambda(t)$, it can be represented by an area under the graph of $\lambda(t)$. This is illustrated in Figure 6.5.

Now consider the number of events that occur in the interval $(t_1, t_2]$ (where $t_2 > t_1$). Since the rate $\lambda(t)$ changes with time, the distribution of the number of events in the interval depends not only on the length of the interval but also on the value of t_1. First note that

$$X(t_1, t_2) = X(0, t_2) - X(0, t_1) = X(t_2) - X(t_1).$$

It follows that the mean of $X(t_1, t_2)$, which is denoted $\mu(t_1, t_2)$, is given by

$$\begin{aligned}\mu(t_1, t_2) = E[X(t_1, t_2)] &= E[X(t_2)] - E[X(t_1)] \\ &= \mu(t_2) - \mu(t_1) \\ &= \int_{t_1}^{t_2} \lambda(u)\, du.\end{aligned}$$

This result is illustrated in Figure 6.6.

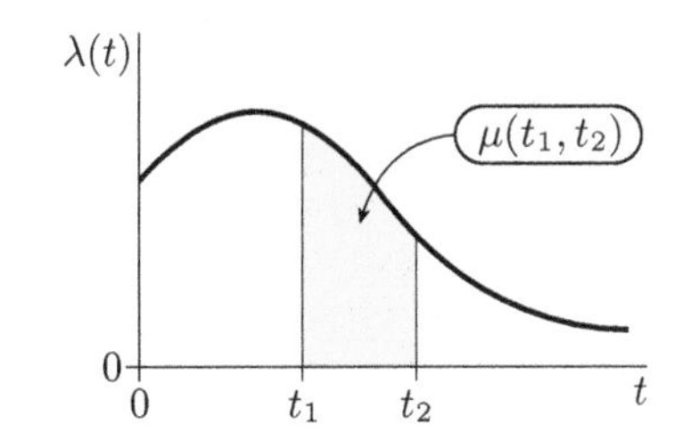

Figure 6.6 The expected number of events in $(t_1, t_2]$

In fact, the number of events occurring in $(t_1, t_2]$ has a Poisson distribution with parameter $\mu(t_1, t_2)$. This result is stated in the following box.

The distribution of $X(t_1, t_2)$

If $X(t_1, t_2)$ is the number of events that occur in a non-homogeneous Poisson process with rate $\lambda(t)$ during the interval $(t_1, t_2]$ (where $t_2 > t_1$), then $X(t_1, t_2)$ has a Poisson distribution with parameter $\mu(t_1, t_2)$:

$$X(t_1, t_2) \sim \text{Poisson}(\mu(t_1, t_2)), \qquad (6.3)$$

where

$$\mu(t_1, t_2) = \mu(t_2) - \mu(t_1). \qquad (6.4)$$

The application of these results is illustrated in Example 6.5.

Example 6.5 Errors in a maze

Suppose that the hourly error rate for a laboratory rat learning its way around a maze is given by

$$\lambda(t) = 8e^{-t}, \quad t \geq 0.$$

This rate is illustrated in Figure 6.7.

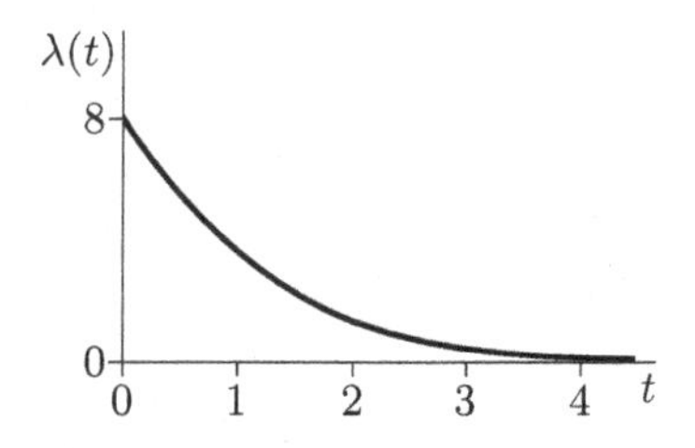

Figure 6.7 The error rate $\lambda(t) = 8e^{-t}$, $t \geq 0$

A good approach in any problem involving a non-homogeneous Poisson process is to begin by finding an expression for $\mu(t)$, whether or not this is asked for explicitly. This can then be used to calculate values of $\mu(t_1)$ and $\mu(t_1, t_2)$ for specific values of t_1 and t_2.

The expected number of errors that the rat makes in its first t hours in the maze – that is, during the interval $(0, t]$ – is given by

$$\mu(t) = \int_0^t \lambda(u)\, du = \int_0^t 8e^{-u}\, du = \left[-8e^{-u}\right]_0^t = 8\left(1 - e^{-t}\right).$$

So, for instance, the expected number of errors in the first hour is

$$\mu(1) = 8\left(1 - e^{-1}\right) \simeq 5.057.$$

This is illustrated in Figure 6.8.

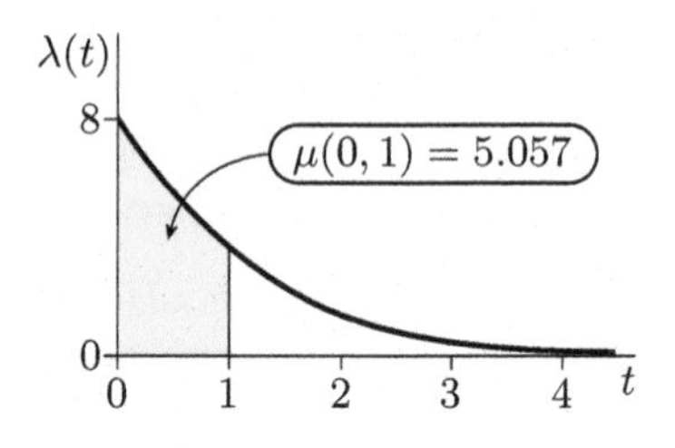

Figure 6.8 The expected number of errors in the first hour, $\mu(0, 1) = \mu(1)$

The expected number of errors that the rat makes during its second hour in the maze is given by

$$\begin{aligned}\mu(1, 2) &= \mu(2) - \mu(1)\\ &= 8\left(1 - e^{-2}\right) - 8\left(1 - e^{-1}\right)\\ &\simeq 1.860.\end{aligned}$$

This is illustrated in Figure 6.9.

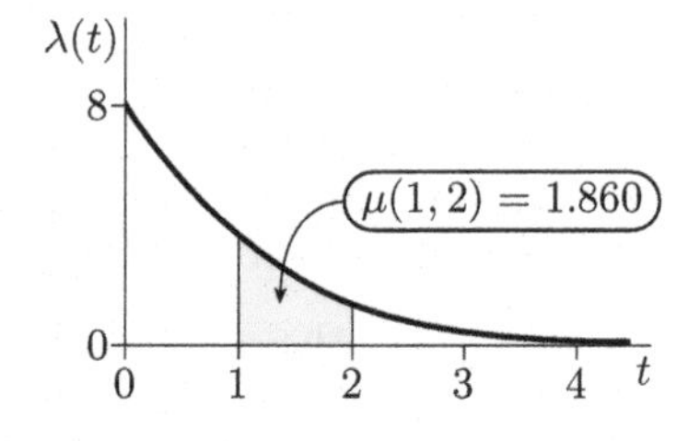

Figure 6.9 The expected number of errors in the second hour, $\mu(1, 2)$

Therefore the number of errors that the rat makes in the second hour, which is denoted $X(1, 2)$, has a Poisson distribution with mean 1.86. Hence, for example, the probability that the rat makes more than two errors in the second hour is

$$\begin{aligned}P(X(1, 2) > 2) &= 1 - P(X(1, 2) \leq 2)\\ &= 1 - e^{-1.86}\left(1 + 1.86 + \frac{1.86^2}{2!}\right)\\ &\simeq 0.285.\end{aligned}$$ ♦

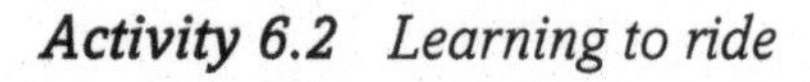

Activity 6.2 Learning to ride

In Example 6.4, the accident rate at time t of a young girl learning to ride a bicycle is given by

$$\lambda(t) = \frac{24}{2 + t}, \quad t \geq 0,$$

where t is measured in days.

(a) Find the expected number of accidents in the first t days.

(b) Calculate the expected number of accidents during the first week.

(c) Calculate the expected number of accidents during the third week. What is the probability that the girl has eight accidents in the third week?

(d) Calculate the probability that the fourth week is free of accidents.

Event times

As for the Poisson process, the distribution of $X(t)$ can be used to obtain the distribution of the waiting time T_1 until the first event. The derivation makes use of the fact that the waiting time to the first event exceeds t if and only if there is no event in $(0, t]$: $[T_1 > t]$ and $[X(t) = 0]$ are equivalent events. It follows that

$$P(T_1 > t) = P(X(t) = 0).$$

Since $X(t) \sim \text{Poisson}(\mu(t))$,

$$P(X(t) = 0) = e^{-\mu(t)},$$

and hence

$$P(T_1 > t) = e^{-\mu(t)}.$$

The c.d.f. of T_1 is

$$F_{T_1}(t) = P(T_1 \leq t) = 1 - P(T_1 > t).$$

So the c.d.f. of the waiting time until the first event is given by

$$F_{T_1}(t) = 1 - e^{-\mu(t)}, \quad t > 0.$$

Similarly, the distribution of $X(t_1, t_2)$ can be used to obtain the distribution of the time T from the start of observation until the next event after some given time v. The time T exceeds t if and only if there is no event in the interval $(v, t]$, so

$$P(T > t) = P(X(v, t) = 0).$$

Since $X(v, t) \sim \text{Poisson}(\mu(v, t))$, it follows that

$$P(T > t) = e^{-\mu(v,t)},$$

and hence the c.d.f. of the time T at which the next event after time v occurs is given by

$$F_T(t) = P(T \leq t) = 1 - e^{-\mu(v,t)}, \quad t > v.$$

These results will be used in Subsection 6.3 to simulate the times $W_1, W_2, \ldots$ at which events occur in a non-homogeneous Poisson process. The results are summarised in the following box.

Times of events

The c.d.f. of T_1, the waiting time until the first event occurs, is

$$F_{T_1}(t) = 1 - e^{-\mu(t)}, \quad t > 0. \tag{6.5}$$

The c.d.f. of T, the time from the start of observation until the first event after time v occurs, is

$$F_T(t) = 1 - e^{-\mu(v,t)}, \quad t > v. \tag{6.6}$$

Activity 6.3 *Event times*

Suppose that events in a non-homogeneous Poisson process occur at the rate

$$\lambda(t) = 2t, \quad t \geq 0.$$

(a) Find the expected number of events that occur by time t.

(b) If observation starts at time $t = 0$, find the probability $P(T_1 > t)$, where T_1 is the waiting time until the first event.

(c) Find $E(T_1)$, the expected waiting time until the first event.

(d) If T is the time from the start of observation until the occurrence of the first event after time v, find $P(T > t)$.

Use the following result from the *Handbook*:

$$\int_{-\infty}^{\infty} e^{-\alpha x^2}\,dx = \sqrt{\frac{\pi}{\alpha}}.$$

6.3 Simulation

In Subsection 3.3, the times of occurrence of events in a Poisson process were simulated by obtaining observations on the inter-event times $T_1, T_2, \ldots$. For a non-homogeneous Poisson process, the times of occurrence of events, $W_1, W_2, \ldots$, can be simulated directly using the probability-integral transformation and Results (6.5) and (6.6). The probability-integral transformation states that an observation x of a continuous random variable X can be simulated by solving the equation $F(x) = u$ for x, where u is a random observation from $U(0,1)$, and $F(x)$ is the c.d.f. of X. The c.d.f. of $W_1 = T_1$, which is given by (6.5), can be used to simulate the time of occurrence of the first event. The times of occurrence of subsequent events, $W_2, W_3, \ldots$, can be simulated using (6.6).

If $F_{W_1}(w)$ is the c.d.f. of W_1, the time at which the first event occurs, then, given a random observation u from $U(0,1)$, a random observation w_1 of W_1 can be obtained by solving the equation $F_{W_1}(w_1) = u$ for w_1. Since $W_1 = T_1$, the c.d.f. of W_1 is given by (6.5), and hence w_1 is found by solving

$$1 - e^{-\mu(w_1)} = u.$$

Rearranging this equation gives

$$e^{-\mu(w_1)} = 1 - u,$$

or equivalently

$$\mu(w_1) = -\log(1-u).$$

The solution w_1 of this equation is the simulated time of occurrence for the first event.

If the jth event occurs at time w_j, then the time at which the $(j+1)$th event occurs can be simulated as follows. Since W_{j+1} is the time at which the next event occurs after time w_j, putting $v = w_j$ in (6.6) gives the c.d.f. of W_{j+1}:

$$F_{W_{j+1}}(t) = 1 - e^{-\mu(w_j,t)} = 1 - e^{-[\mu(t)-\mu(w_j)]}.$$

A random observation w_{j+1} of W_{j+1} can be obtained by solving for w_{j+1} the equation

$$1 - e^{-[\mu(w_{j+1})-\mu(w_j)]} = u,$$

where u is a random observation from $U(0,1)$. Rearranging this equation gives

$$e^{-[\mu(w_{j+1})-\mu(w_j)]} = 1 - u,$$

or equivalently

$$\mu(w_{j+1}) - \mu(w_j) = -\log(1-u),$$

which can be written as

$$\mu(w_{j+1}) = \mu(w_j) - \log(1-u).$$

These results for simulating the times at which events occur in a non-homogeneous Poisson process are summarised in the following box.

Simulation for a non-homogeneous Poisson process

Given a random observation u from $U(0,1)$, the simulated time of occurrence of the first event in a non-homogeneous Poisson process is w_1, where w_1 is the solution of

$$\mu(w_1) = -\log(1-u). \tag{6.7}$$

Suppose that the jth event occurs at time w_j, $j = 1, 2, \ldots$. Then, given a random observation u from $U(0,1)$, the simulated time at which the $(j+1)$th event occurs is w_{j+1}, where w_{j+1} is obtained by solving

$$\mu(w_{j+1}) = \mu(w_j) - \log(1-u). \tag{6.8}$$

Notice that if j is set equal to 0 in (6.8) and w_0 is defined to be equal to 0, then (6.8) can be used as the formula to generate the simulated time w_1 as well as all subsequent times $w_2, w_3, \ldots$.

Example 6.6 Simulating errors made by a rat

In Example 6.5, it was shown that the expected number of errors that a laboratory rat makes during its first t hours in a maze is given by

$$\mu(t) = 8\left(1 - e^{-t}\right).$$

The random numbers $u_1 = 0.964\,17$, $u_2 = 0.633\,36$ and $u_3 = 0.884\,91$ will be used to simulate the times at which the rat makes its first three errors.

Using (6.7), the simulated time w_1 at which the first error is made is the solution of

$$\mu(w_1) = -\log(1 - u_1) = -\log(1 - 0.964\,17) \simeq 3.3290.$$

Solving

$$8\left(1 - e^{-w_1}\right) = 3.3290$$

leads to

$$e^{-w_1} = 1 - \frac{3.3290}{8} = 0.583\,875,$$

giving

$$w_1 \simeq 0.538\,07 \text{ hours} \simeq 32 \text{ minutes}.$$

The simulated time w_2 for the rat's second error is found using (6.8):

$$\mu(w_2) = \mu(w_1) - \log(1 - u_2) = 3.3290 - \log(1 - 0.633\,36) \simeq 4.3324.$$

Solving

$$8\left(1 - e^{-w_2}\right) = 4.3324$$

leads to

$$w_2 \simeq 0.779\,90 \text{ hours} \simeq 47 \text{ minutes}.$$

Using (6.8) again, the simulated time w_3 for the rat's third error can be found:

$$\mu(w_3) = \mu(w_2) - \log(1 - u_3) = 4.3324 - \log(1 - 0.884\,91) \simeq 6.4944.$$

Solving

$$8\left(1 - e^{-w_3}\right) = 6.4944$$

leads to

$$w_3 \simeq 1.670\,25 \text{ hours} \simeq 1 \text{ hour } 40 \text{ minutes}.$$

In this simulation the rat makes its first three errors 32 minutes, 47 minutes and 1 hour 40 minutes after entering the maze. ♦

Activity 6.4 Simulating times of events

The rate at which events occur in the non-homogeneous Poisson process of Activity 6.3 is

$$\lambda(t) = 2t, \quad t \geq 0.$$

Simulate the times at which the first three events occur in a realisation of the process. Use the numbers $u_1 = 0.622$, $u_2 = 0.239$, $u_3 = 0.775$, which are random observations from $U(0,1)$.

The calculations involved in simulating the times of events in a non-homogeneous Poisson process can sometimes be simplified by solving Formula (6.8) algebraically to obtain a recurrence relation for the simulated times $w_1, w_2, w_3, \ldots$. This is illustrated in Example 6.7.

Example 6.7 Simulating times of machine malfunctions

Occasionally a machine malfunctions, resulting in the production of defective items. The incidence of these malfunctions may be modelled as a non-homogeneous Poisson process with rate

$$\lambda(t) = \frac{2t}{1+t^2}, \quad t \geq 0.$$

The expected number of events in the interval $(0, t]$ is given by

$$\begin{aligned}\mu(t) = \int_0^t \lambda(v)\,dv = \int_0^t \frac{2v}{1+v^2}\,dv \\ &= \left[\log(1+v^2)\right]_0^t \\ &= \log(1+t^2) - \log(1) \\ &= \log(1+t^2).\end{aligned}$$

The times of machine malfunctions can be simulated using Formula (6.8):

$$\mu(w_{j+1}) = \mu(w_j) - \log(1-u).$$

In this case, this gives

$$\log(1+w_{j+1}^2) = \log(1+w_j^2) - \log(1-u).$$

This can be rearranged to give w_{j+1} explicitly, as follows. Taking exponentials gives

$$1 + w_{j+1}^2 = \frac{1+w_j^2}{1-u},$$

so that

$$w_{j+1}^2 = \frac{1+w_j^2}{1-u} - 1 = \frac{(1+w_j^2)-(1-u)}{1-u} = \frac{w_j^2+u}{1-u},$$

and hence

$$w_{j+1} = \sqrt{\frac{w_j^2+u}{1-u}}.$$

This recurrence relation can be used to simulate the occurrence of malfunctions during the interval $(0, 2]$. Using numbers from the fourth row of Table 5 in the *Handbook* (25727, 64334, ...) gives the following simulated times:

$$w_1 = \sqrt{\frac{0^2+0.257\,27}{1-0.257\,27}} \simeq 0.5885,$$

Recall that w_1 can be found by setting $w_0 = 0$ in (6.8).

$$w_2 = \sqrt{\frac{0.5885^2+0.643\,34}{1-0.643\,34}} \simeq 1.6658,$$

$$w_3 = \sqrt{\frac{1.6658^2+0.086\,91}{1-0.086\,91}} \simeq 1.7704,$$

$$w_4 = \sqrt{\frac{1.7704^2+0.189\,12}{1-0.189\,12}} \simeq 2.0245.$$

Retaining full calculator accuracy throughout also leads to $w_4 \simeq 2.0245$.

The fourth event occurs after time 2, so there are three malfunctions in $(0, 2]$ in this simulation, and these occur at times $w_1 \simeq 0.5885$, $w_2 \simeq 1.6658$, $w_3 \simeq 1.7704$. ♦

Activity 6.5 Another simulation

Show that for the non-homogeneous Poisson process of Activities 6.3 and 6.4, which has rate $\lambda(t) = 2t$, $t \geq 0$, the times at which events occur can be simulated using the recurrence relation

$$w_{j+1} = \sqrt{w_j^2 - \log(1-u)}.$$

Hence simulate the times of the first four events in a realisation of the process. Use the numbers $u_1 = 0.927$, $u_2 = 0.098$, $u_3 = 0.397$, $u_4 = 0.604$, which are random observations from $U(0,1)$.

Summary of Section 6

The non-homogeneous Poisson process is a model for events occurring at random in time at a rate that changes with time. The distribution of the number of events in an interval has been used to calculate probabilities, and you have learned how to simulate the times at which events occur.

Exercises on Section 6

Exercise 6.1 A non-homogeneous Poisson process

Events occur according to a non-homogeneous Poisson process with rate

$$\lambda(t) = \tfrac{3}{8}t^2(4-t), \quad 0 \leq t \leq 4.$$

(a) Sketch the function $\lambda(t)$ for t between 0 and 4, and show on your sketch the expected number of events between $t = 1$ and $t = 2$.

(b) Find $\mu(t)$, the expected number of events that occur by time t.

(c) Find the expected number of events between $t = 1$ and $t = 3$, and the expected total number of events (that is, between $t = 0$ and $t = 4$).

(d) Calculate the probability that more than two events occur between $t = 1$ and $t = 3$.

(e) Given that two events occur between $t = 0$ and $t = 1$, calculate the probability that at least four events occur in total (that is, between $t = 0$ and $t = 4$).

Exercise 6.2 Simulation

Simulate the occurrences of events in the interval $(0,1]$ in a non-homogeneous Poisson process with rate $\lambda(t) = 3t^2$. Use random numbers from the third row of the table of random digits in the *Handbook* (beginning $u_1 = 0.240\,36$, $u_2 = 0.290\,38$, $\ldots$).

7 The compound Poisson process

One of the assumptions of the Poisson process is that events always occur one at a time: there are no multiple occurrences. In this section, the Poisson process is extended to the situation where multiple occurrences are allowed. An example of this sort of situation was described in Example 3.1: the occurrence of major earthquakes may be modelled by a Poisson process, each earthquake resulting in a number of fatalities. Several more examples are described below.

Example 7.1 Arrivals by bus

Buses arrive at a shopping centre according to a Poisson process at the rate of one bus per minute. Let $X(t)$ denote the number of buses that arrive in an interval of length t hours. Suppose that the number of passengers that disembark from each bus is an independent observation on the discrete random variable Y. Then $S(t)$, the total number of passengers disembarking during the interval, is given by

$$S(t) = Y_1 + Y_2 + \cdots + Y_{X(t)},$$

where Y_i is the number of passengers that disembark from the ith bus. ♦

Example 7.2 Visitors to a restaurant

Between 12 noon and 2 pm, private cars call at a roadside restaurant according to a Poisson process at the rate of one car every four minutes. If $X(2)$ is the number of cars that arrive in the two-hour period, then $X(2)$ has a Poisson distribution with parameter 30. Suppose that the number of occupants in each car is an observation on the discrete random variable Y with the geometric distribution $G_1(0.4)$. Then $S(2)$, the total number of visitors to the restaurant over the two-hour period, is given by

$\lambda = 15$ per hour and $t = 2$ hours, so $\lambda t = 30$.

$$S(2) = Y_1 + Y_2 + \cdots + Y_{X(2)},$$

where $X(2) \sim \text{Poisson}(30)$ and each Y_i has the given geometric distribution. ♦

Example 7.3 Recorded events

Events occur in time according to a Poisson process with rate λ. However, each event has only probability p of being detected and recorded, independently of whether or not other events are recorded. Thus associated with each event is the random variable Y that takes the value 1 if the event is recorded and 0 if it is not. If $X(t)$ is the number of events that occur in an interval of length t, then the number of events recorded in the interval is given by

$$S(t) = Y_1 + Y_2 + \cdots + Y_{X(t)},$$

where $Y_i \sim B(1,p)$ and $X(t)$ has a Poisson distribution with parameter λt. ♦

In Examples 7.1 to 7.3, events occur according to a Poisson process, and associated with each event is another event for which multiple occurrences are possible. The number of occurrences associated with each event in the Poisson process is an observation on a discrete random variable Y. Such a process is called a **compound Poisson process**. Each event of the Poisson process is referred to as a **compound event**. If the number of compound events that occur in $(0,t]$ is denoted $X(t)$, and the number of occurrences associated with the ith compound event is Y_i, then $S(t)$, the total number of occurrences of events in the interval $(0,t]$, is given by

$$S(t) = Y_1 + Y_2 + \cdots + Y_{X(t)}.$$

In *Book 1*, several results for sums of random variables were given. However, these results apply only when the number of random variables in the sum is known. Since $S(t)$ is the sum of $X(t)$ random variables and $X(t)$ is itself a random variable, the number of random variables in the sum is not known. Therefore the results cannot be used to obtain information about $S(t)$.

In this section, expressions for the mean and variance of $S(t)$ will be found. You will not be expected to reproduce the derivation. However, you should try to follow the arguments used.

The probability distribution of $S(t)$ will be found using probability generating functions in *Book 3*.

The mean and variance of Y, the number of occurrences associated with each compound event, will be denoted μ and σ^2, respectively, so

$$E(Y) = \mu, \quad V(Y) = \sigma^2.$$

The mean of $S(t)$

The mean of $S(t)$ is given by

$$E[S(t)] = \sum_{s=0}^{\infty} s\,P(S(t) = s).$$

Since $X(t)$ must take just one of the values $x = 0, 1 \ldots$, the events $[X(t) = 0]$, $[X(t) = 1]$, ... are mutually exclusive and exhaustive. Hence, by the Theorem of Total Probability,

$$P(S(t) = s) = \sum_{x=0}^{\infty} P(S(t) = s \mid X(t) = x)\,P(X(t) = x).$$

Thus $E[S(t)]$ can be written as

$$E[S(t)] = \sum_{s=0}^{\infty} s \sum_{x=0}^{\infty} P(S(t) = s \mid X(t) = x)\,P(X(t) = x).$$

Interchanging the order of summation on the right-hand side gives

$$E[S(t)] = \sum_{x=0}^{\infty} P(X(t) = x) \sum_{s=0}^{\infty} s\,P(S(t) = s \mid X(t) = x). \tag{7.1}$$

The sum over s is simply the expected value of $S(t)$ when $X(t)$ takes the particular value x; that is, it is the conditional expectation $E[S(t) \mid X(t) = x]$. So (7.1) can be written as

$$E[S(t)] = \sum_{x=0}^{\infty} P(X(t) = x)\,E[S(t) \mid X(t) = x]. \tag{7.2}$$

When $X(t)$ is equal to x, $S(t)$ is the sum of a fixed number, x, of random variables Y_i: $S(t) = Y_1 + Y_2 + \cdots + Y_x$. Since the Y_i $(i = 1, \ldots, x)$ are identically distributed with mean μ, the expected value of $Y_1 + Y_2 + \cdots + Y_x$ is $x\mu$. That is,

$$E[S(t) \mid X(t) = x] = x\mu.$$

Substituting this in (7.2) gives

$$E[S(t)] = \sum_{x=0}^{\infty} P(X(t) = x)\,x\mu = \mu \sum_{x=0}^{\infty} x\,P(X(t) = x) = \mu\,E[X(t)]. \tag{7.3}$$

Since $X(t)$ is the number of events occurring in time t in a Poisson process with rate λ, $X(t) \sim \text{Poisson}(\lambda t)$, and hence $E[X(t)] = \lambda t$. Substituting λt for $E[X(t)]$ in (7.3) leads to the following result: the expected number of events in an interval of length t is

$$E[S(t)] = \mu\lambda t.$$

You might have expected this result intuitively, since λt compound events are expected in the interval $(0, t]$, and μ is the mean number of events associated with each compound event.

The variance of $S(t)$

A formula for the variance of $S(t)$ can be obtained using a similar method.

First note that the variance of any random variable X is given by

$$V(X) = E(X^2) - (E(X))^2,$$

so that

$$E(X^2) = V(X) + (E(X))^2.$$

In particular, for $i = 1, 2, \ldots$,

$$E(Y_i^2) = V(Y_i) + (E(Y_i))^2 = \sigma^2 + \mu^2. \quad (7.4)$$

The variance of $S(t)$ is

$$V[S(t)] = E\left[(S(t))^2\right] - (E[S(t)])^2.$$

An expression for $E[(S(t)]$ has just been obtained: $E[S(t)] = \mu\lambda t$. So it remains to find $E\left[(S(t))^2\right]$. In (7.2), $E[S(t)]$ was written in terms of the conditional expectations $E[S(t) \mid X(t) = x]$. Similarly, $E\left[(S(t))^2\right]$ can be written in terms of the conditional expectations $E\left[(S(t))^2 \mid X(t) = x\right]$. A similar argument to that used to obtain (7.2) leads to

$$E\left[(S(t))^2\right] = \sum_{x=0}^{\infty} P(X(t) = x)\, E\left[(S(t))^2 \mid X(t) = x\right].$$

When $X(t) = x$, $S(t) = Y_1 + Y_2 + \cdots + Y_x$, so

$$\begin{aligned} E\left[(S(t))^2 \mid X(t) = x\right] &= E\left[(Y_1 + Y_2 + \cdots + Y_x)^2\right] \\ &= E\big[Y_1^2 + (Y_1Y_2 + Y_1Y_3 + \cdots + Y_1Y_x) \\ &\qquad + Y_2^2 + (Y_2Y_1 + Y_2Y_3 + \cdots + Y_2Y_x) \\ &\qquad \vdots \\ &\qquad + Y_x^2 + (Y_xY_1 + Y_xY_2 + \cdots + Y_xY_{x-1})\big]. \end{aligned}$$

In this sum, there are x terms of the form $E(Y_i^2)$ and $x(x-1)$ terms of the form $E(Y_iY_j)$ where $i \neq j$. From (7.4), $E(Y_i^2) = \sigma^2 + \mu^2$. And, since Y_i and Y_j are independent with mean μ, it follows that $E(Y_iY_j) = E(Y_i)\,E(Y_j) = \mu^2$.

Therefore

$$\begin{aligned} E\left[(S(t))^2 \mid X(t) = x\right] &= x\,E(Y_i^2) + x(x-1)\,E(Y_iY_j) \\ &= x(\sigma^2 + \mu^2) + x(x-1)\mu^2 \\ &= x\sigma^2 + x^2\mu^2. \end{aligned}$$

Using this result gives

$$\begin{aligned} E\left[(S(t))^2\right] &= \sum_{x=0}^{\infty} P(X(t) = x)\, E\left[(S(t))^2 \mid X(t) = x\right] \\ &= \sum_{x=0}^{\infty} P(X(t) = x)\left(x\sigma^2 + x^2\mu^2\right) \\ &= \sigma^2 \sum_{x=0}^{\infty} x\,P(X(t) = x) + \mu^2 \sum_{x=0}^{\infty} x^2\,P(X(t) = x) \\ &= \sigma^2\,E[X(t)] + \mu^2\,E\left[X(t)^2\right] \\ &= \sigma^2\,E[X(t)] + \mu^2\left(V[X(t)] + (E[X(t)])^2\right). \end{aligned}$$

Since $X(t) \sim \text{Poisson}(\lambda t)$, it follows that $E[X(t)] = V[X(t)] = \lambda t$, and hence

$$E\left[(S(t))^2\right] = \sigma^2\lambda t + \mu^2\left(\lambda t + (\lambda t)^2\right).$$

Therefore

$$\begin{aligned} V[S(t)] &= E\left[(S(t))^2\right] - (E[S(t)])^2 \\ &= \sigma^2\lambda t + \mu^2\left(\lambda t + (\lambda t)^2\right) - (\mu\lambda t)^2 \\ &= \sigma^2\lambda t + \mu^2\lambda t + \mu^2(\lambda t)^2 - (\mu\lambda t)^2 \\ &= \lambda t(\sigma^2 + \mu^2). \end{aligned}$$

These results for a compound Poisson process are stated in the following box.

Compound Poisson process

In a **compound Poisson process**, compound events occur in time according to a Poisson process with rate λ, and associated with each compound event is another event for which multiple occurrences are possible.

If $S(t)$ is the total number of events that occur in $(0, t]$, then

$$E[S(t)] = \mu\lambda t, \tag{7.5}$$

$$V[S(t)] = \lambda t(\sigma^2 + \mu^2), \tag{7.6}$$

where μ and σ^2 are the mean and variance of the number of events associated with each compound event.

Example 7.4 Visitors to a restaurant

In Example 7.2, Y_i, the number of occupants in each car calling at a roadside restaurant, is an observation on a geometric random variable: $Y_i \sim G_1(0.4)$. Therefore

$$\mu = E(Y_i) = \frac{1}{0.4} = 2.5,$$

$$\sigma^2 = V(Y_i) = \frac{0.6}{0.4^2} = 3.75.$$

The mean and variance of the geometric distribution $G_1(p)$ are $1/p$ and q/p^2, respectively.

Cars arrive according to a Poisson process with rate $\lambda = 15$ per hour during the two-hour period from 12 noon to 2 pm. Using (7.5) and (7.6) with $\lambda = 15$ and $t = 2$, the mean and variance of $S(2)$, the total number of people visiting the restaurant over the two-hour period, are

$$E[S(2)] = 2.5 \times 15 \times 2 = 75,$$

$$V[S(2)] = 15 \times 2 \times (3.75 + 2.5^2) = 300. \quad \blacklozenge$$

Activity 7.1 Items purchased

Suppose that shoppers leave a village shop according to a Poisson process at the rate of one every five minutes. Independently of one another, each shopper purchases Y items, where Y has the following probability distribution.

y	0	1	2	3
$P(Y = y)$	0.2	0.3	0.4	0.1

(a) Calculate the mean and variance of Y.

(b) Calculate the mean and variance of the total number of items purchased in a three-hour period.

Activity 7.2 Road casualties

Suppose that road accidents occur according to a Poisson process with rate λ and that Y_i, the number of casualties in the ith accident ($i = 1, 2, \ldots$), has a geometric distribution: $Y_i \sim G_0(\alpha)$, $0 < \alpha < 1$. Find the mean and variance of the number of casualties that occur in an interval of length t.

Activity 7.3 Events recorded

Suppose that events occur according to a Poisson process with rate λ and that each event has probability p of being detected and recorded.

(a) Find the mean and variance of the number of events recorded in the interval $(0, t]$.

(b) From your answers to part (a), what do you think the probability distribution of the number of detected events might be? How could you have known this?

Summary of Section 7

The compound Poisson process is an extension of the Poisson process that allows for multiple occurrences of events. Events, called compound events, occur according to a Poisson process, and associated with each compound event is another event for which multiple occurrences are possible. In this section, formulas have been derived for the mean and variance of the total number of events that occur in an interval of length t.

Exercises on Section 7

Exercise 7.1 Complaints

Letters arrive at a company's complaints centre according to a Poisson process at the rate of eighteen letters a day (five days a week); Y, the number of complaints per letter, has the following probability distribution.

y	0	1	2	3
$P(Y = y)$	0.03	0.84	0.12	0.01

The event $Y = 0$ corresponds to the situation where customers merely wish to offer the company the benefit of their advice.

(a) Find the mean and variance of the random variable Y.

(b) Find the mean and variance of the total number of complaints that arrive at the centre over any four-week period.

Exercise 7.2 Unscheduled maintenance

A car hire company rents out vehicles to customers according to a Poisson process at the rate of 60 rentals per week. For each vehicle hired out, the number of minor dents, abrasions and other items requiring unscheduled attention on its return has a Poisson distribution with mean 0.8. Calculate the mean and variance of the number of unscheduled tasks required of the company's maintenance staff over a four-week period.

8 Point processes

A random process that consists of events occurring in time is known as a **point process**. The models studied in Part II, all of which are based on the Poisson process, are examples of point processes. In Subsection 8.1, point processes are discussed briefly in more general terms, and a method of comparing a point process with a Poisson process is introduced. A few further examples of point processes are described briefly in Subsection 8.2.

8.1 The index of dispersion

In this subsection, a measure for comparing point processes based on the distribution of the number of events that occur in a fixed time interval is discussed.

For a point process, the **index of dispersion**, denoted $I(t)$, is defined by

$$I(t) = \frac{V[X(t)]}{E[X(t)]},$$

where $X(t)$ is the number of events that occur in $(0, t]$.

For a Poisson process with rate λ, $X(t) \sim \text{Poisson}(\lambda t)$, so $E[X(t)] = V[X(t)] = \lambda t$, and hence $I(t) = 1$. For other point processes the value of $I(t)$ may be different from 1, and this fact can be used to compare any point process with a Poisson process.

Suppose that in a point process $E[X(t)]$ is equal to λt, but the events occur in a more regular fashion than in a Poisson process with rate λ. Then $V[X(t)]$ will be smaller than λt, and hence the index of dispersion for the process will be less than 1. On the other hand, if there is more dispersion in a point process than in a Poisson process with the same rate, so that very long and very short intervals are more likely to arise than in the Poisson process, then the index of dispersion for the process will be greater than 1.

Example 8.1 The multivariate Poisson process

In Section 5, you saw that the multivariate Poisson process, which consists of events of different types each occurring as a Poisson process, is just a Poisson process with rate equal to the sum of the rates of the component processes. Hence the index of dispersion for this process is equal to 1. ♦

Activity 8.1 The non-homogeneous Poisson process

Calculate the index of dispersion for a non-homogeneous Poisson process.

The compound Poisson process with rate λ, in which multiple occurrences are permitted, was discussed in Section 7. For the compound Poisson process, the number of events in $(0, t]$ is denoted $S(t)$. Formulas for $E[S(t)]$ and $V[S(t)]$ were derived in Section 7:

$$E[S(t)] = \mu\lambda t,$$
$$V[S(t)] = \lambda t(\sigma^2 + \mu^2),$$

These are Results (7.5) and (7.6).

where μ and σ^2 are the mean and variance of the number of events in each compound event. Therefore the index of dispersion for the compound Poisson process is

$$I(t) = \frac{V[S(t)]}{E[S(t)]} = \frac{\lambda t(\sigma^2 + \mu^2)}{\mu\lambda t} = \frac{\sigma^2}{\mu} + \mu. \qquad (8.1)$$

Example 8.2 Visitors to a restaurant

In the situation described in Example 7.4, cars arrive at a roadside restaurant according to a Poisson process, and the number of occupants in each car is a random variable with mean $\mu = 2.5$ and variance $\sigma^2 = 3.75$. Thus, using (8.1), the index of dispersion for the compound Poisson process is

$$I(t) = \frac{\sigma^2}{\mu} + \mu = \frac{3.75}{2.5} + 2.5 = 4.$$

Since $I(t) > 1$, the arrivals of people visiting the restaurant are more variable than they would be if people arrived according to a Poisson process. ♦

Activity 8.2 Items purchased

A compound Poisson process of purchases of items from a village shop is described in Activity 7.1.

(a) Calculate the index of dispersion for the compound Poisson process.

(b) What does the value of the index of dispersion tell you about the pattern of purchases?

Activity 8.3 Road casualties

In Activity 7.2, casualties in road accidents were modelled by a compound Poisson process. The number of casualties in each accident has the geometric distribution $G_0(\alpha)$, $0 < \alpha < 1$. Find the index of dispersion for the process.

Activity 8.4 Another compound Poisson process

Find the index of dispersion for a compound Poisson process when Y, the number of events at each compound event, has a Poisson distribution with parameter μ.

In Activity 8.3, you found the index of dispersion for a compound Poisson process for which $Y \sim G_0(\alpha)$. This can be written as

$$I(t) = \frac{1+\alpha}{1-\alpha} = 1 + \frac{2\alpha}{1-\alpha} = 1 + 2\mu,$$

where $\mu = E(Y)$. In Activity 8.4, $Y \sim \text{Poisson}(\mu)$, and the index of dispersion for the compound Poisson process is $1 + \mu$. In each case, the index of dispersion is of the form

$$I(t) = 1 + \text{a positive expression involving } \mu.$$

Therefore $I(t)$ is greater than 1, and hence the compound Poisson process with rate λ displays more variability than does a Poisson process with rate λ. This is a reasonable result, because in the compound Poisson process there is variability not only in the occurrence of compound events but also in the number of events associated with each compound event.

8.2 Types of point process

One type of point process is known as a 'renewal process'. In a renewal process, the times between successive events are independent and identically distributed, but the distribution can take any form. This type of process gets its name from the practical situation where components, such as light bulbs, spark plugs, and so on, wear out and fail and are then immediately replaced or renewed. Thus at each renewal the process starts again, and the lifetimes of components are independent. Since the replacement components are identical, the lifetimes all have the same distribution. The Poisson process is a renewal process with exponentially distributed inter-event times. Since the exponential distribution has the memoryless property, the probability that an event occurs in the small time interval $[t, t + \delta t]$ does not depend on the time at which the previous event occurred. The Poisson process is the only renewal process for which this is the case. In general, in a renewal process, the probability that an event occurs in a small time interval does depend on when the previous event occurred. Renewal processes are studied in *Book 5*.

Another set of possible models for point processes arises when the probability that an event occurs in a specific time interval depends on the *number* of events that have occurred previously. Some processes of this type are studied in *Book 4*.

Point processes for which events can occur only at discrete time points include the Bernoulli process, which is the discrete analogue of the Poisson process and has many of the same properties. In practice, point processes in discrete time occur much less frequently than do those in continuous time.

Summary of Section 8

Point processes have been discussed briefly in this section, and the index of dispersion has been introduced. The index of dispersion for a Poisson process is equal to 1. You have seen that for a multivariate Poisson process and a non-homogeneous Poisson process, the index of dispersion is also equal to 1, but that for many compound Poisson processes the index of dispersion is greater than 1, indicating that occurrences of events are more variable than events in a Poisson process.

Exercises on Section 8

Exercise 8.1 Complaints

Calculate the index of dispersion for the process of arrivals of complaints described in Exercise 7.1. What does the value of the index of dispersion tell you about the pattern of arrivals of complaints?

Exercise 8.2 Unscheduled maintenance

Calculate the index of dispersion for the process of unscheduled maintenance tasks described in Exercise 7.2. What does the value of the index of dispersion tell you about the pattern of occurrences of unscheduled maintenance tasks?

Part III Patterns in space

Introduction to Part III

Patterns in space are the subject of Part III. The main way in which these patterns differ from patterns of events in time is that they usually occur in more than one dimension. Most of the patterns discussed in this book are two-dimensional patterns spread over an area of land – for example, animals grazing in a field, oak trees in a wood, or shops in a town. Three-dimensional patterns, such as dust particles in a room, stars in a galaxy, or galaxies in the universe, are more complicated and will not be considered.

The sorts of questions about a spatial pattern that are of interest include the following. Can the objects in a particular pattern be taken to be randomly distributed over the area that they occupy? Indeed, what does 'randomly distributed' mean? If the pattern is not random, how can it be described and what are its characteristics? What is a plausible probability model for the underlying process? What kinds of pattern are there? These are some of the questions that will be discussed.

In Section 9, several examples of spatial patterns are described. This section is introductory and does not contain any activities. The two-dimensional forms of the two basic patterns in one dimension – the Bernoulli process and the Poisson process – are introduced in Section 10. There are two main ways in which patterns can differ from these basic patterns: either there is some attraction between objects – for example, grazing animals might group together in families – and this produces a pattern that shows clustering; or objects may for some reason not be found very close together – for example, each animal may have its own exclusive grazing territory – and this produces some regularity in the pattern. Probability models for these two situations are described briefly in Section 11. The variability in the distance between neighbouring objects in a spatial pattern is discussed in Section 12. Some of the ideas introduced in this section are used in Section 13, where two hypothesis tests for investigating whether a given pattern is consistent with a two-dimensional Poisson process are described. You will need to be familiar with the basic ideas of fixed-level testing for this section.

9 Spatial patterns

In this section, different types of pattern are illustrated and some ideas and terminology are introduced through a series of examples.

Example 9.1 Free-flowing traffic

Figure 9.1 shows the positions of vehicles on the eastbound carriageway of the Great West Road at Heston.

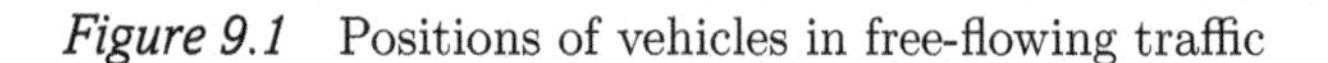

Figure 9.1 Positions of vehicles in free-flowing traffic

This diagram was derived from part of an aerial photograph of the traffic. Each dot represents the front of the bonnet of a vehicle. The lengths of the vehicles are ignored, and all vehicles are represented on a single line, although actually the road has three lanes, each containing some vehicles. The road was busy, but the traffic was flowing freely. ♦

Example 9.2 Heavy traffic

Figure 9.2 shows, in a similar way to Figure 9.1, the positions of vehicles in an eastbound stream of traffic on the coast road from Blackpool to Preston.

Figure 9.2 Positions of vehicles in heavy traffic

The road has only a single lane in each direction. Figure 9.2 is derived from an aerial photograph, taken on a Sunday evening when the road was very congested. Most of the objects (vehicles in this case) shown in Figure 9.2 are spaced quite regularly; this road was essentially full and the vehicles were as close as possible. ♦

Each of Figures 9.1 and 9.2 illustrates a pattern of objects in one-dimensional space, but the patterns are very different. In Figure 9.1, some objects are closely bunched together, but there are also some long gaps. On the other hand, in Figure 9.2, the objects are much more regularly spaced.

Several patterns of objects in two-dimensional space, and their properties, are described in Examples 9.3 to 9.6.

Example 9.3 Oak trees in a wood

Figure 9.3 shows the positions of 211 trees of the white oak species growing within a square-shaped area of 19.6 acres in Lansing Woods, Michigan.

Source of data: Dr D.J. Gerrard; diagram reproduced from Trevor F. Cox (1976) *Some Problems in the Analysis of Spatial Pattern*, PhD thesis, University of Hull.

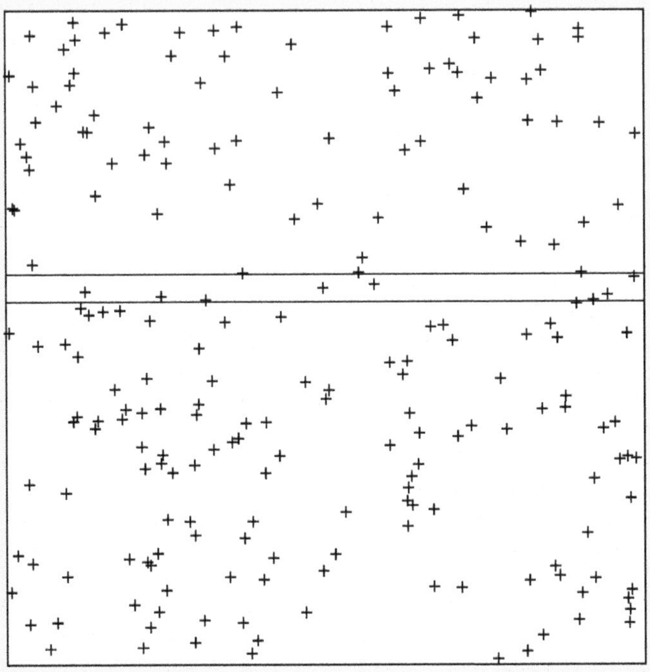

Figure 9.3 The positions of 211 white oak trees in Lansing Woods, Michigan

White oaks are just one of several species of tree growing in these woods. The white oaks are not spaced evenly through the wood: there are some very sparse areas and some areas where the trees are growing much more densely.

A narrow strip or **transect** is marked on Figure 9.3. The positions of trees in this transect, represented as points along a straight line, are shown in Figure 9.4.

Figure 9.4 White oak trees along a transect

This is a one-dimensional pattern of objects derived from the two-dimensional pattern of Figure 9.3. ♦

Example 9.4 London post offices

Figure 9.5 shows the locations of the 62 post offices in a rectangular area of central London, approximately 6 km E/W by 4.5 km N/S. There are no post offices (obviously) in the parks, but otherwise there is a fairly even spread.

These are the locations of post offices in the area in the mid-1980s.

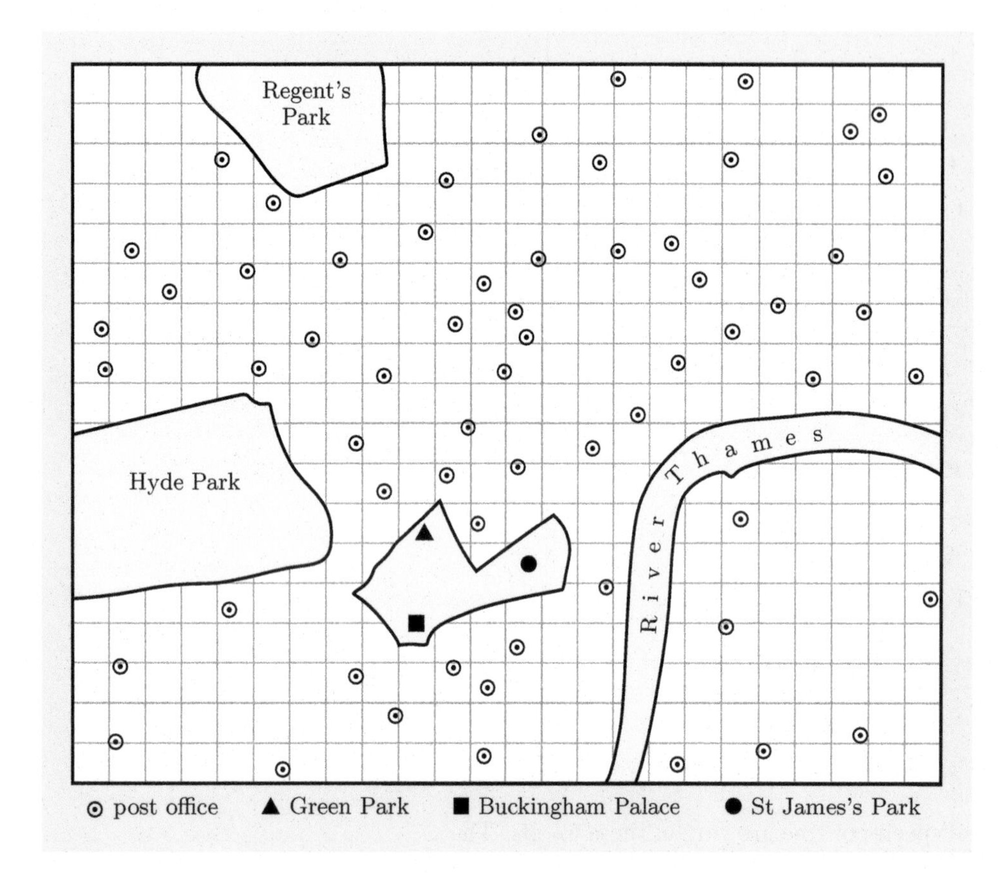

Figure 9.5 Post offices in London ♦

Example 9.5 Redwood seedlings

The positions of 194 redwood seedlings found on a square experimental plot are shown in Figure 9.6.

Strauss, D.J. (1975) 'A model for clustering', *Biometrika*, vol. 62, no. 2, pp. 467–75.

The original paper refers to a total of 199 seedlings, 77 of them in region I. The diagram does not show as many as that.

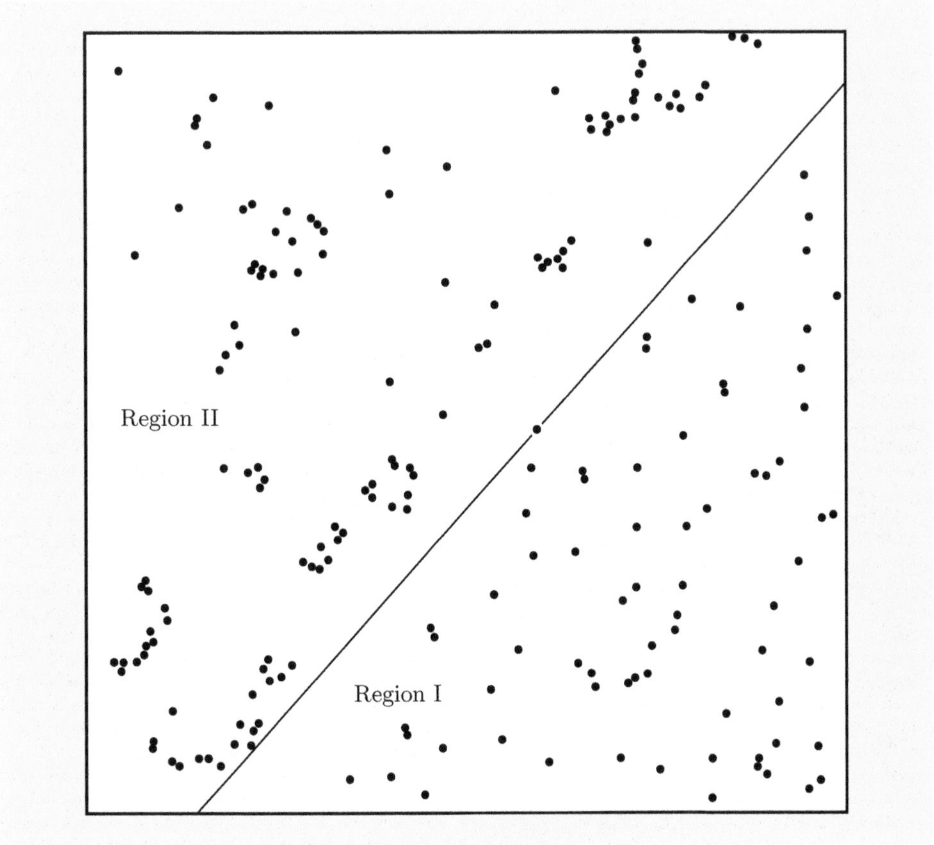

Figure 9.6 Redwood seedlings on an experimental plot

It was thought that seedlings would be scattered fairly randomly except that clusters of seedlings would appear round the old redwood tree stumps present in the plot. A discontinuity in the soil, very roughly marked by the diagonal line in Figure 9.6, might be expected to cause different types of pattern in region I (72 seedlings) and region II (122 seedlings). ♦

Example 9.6 Ants' nests

Figure 9.7 shows the sites of the nests of two species of ant, *Messor wasmanni* and *Cataglyphis bicolor*, in an area measuring approximately 90 m × 90 m in northern Greece.

Harkness, R.D. and Isham, V. (1983) 'A bivariate spatial point pattern of ants' nests', *Applied Statistics*, vol. 32, no. 2, pp. 293–303.

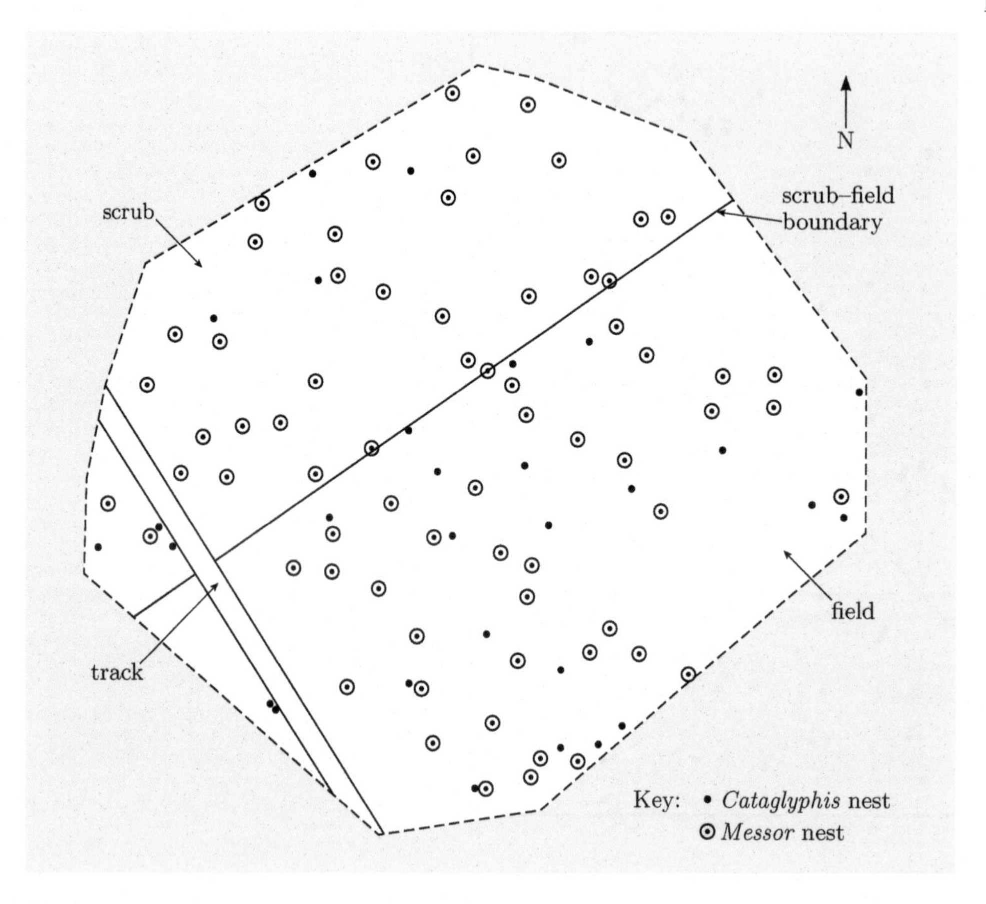

Figure 9.7 Ants' nests

The region is divided into two main parts: the north-west part is open scrubland, and the south-east is a field. Ants cannot build nests at some sites in the scrub where bushes are growing. There is a track down the west side of the region. Altogether there are 68 *Messor* nests and 29 *Cataglyphis* nests. ♦

In all these examples, the figures show the positions of objects observed at a particular instant of time. The objects are vehicles in Examples 9.1 and 9.2, trees in Example 9.3, post offices in Example 9.4, seedlings in Example 9.5, and ants' nests in Example 9.6. In Example 9.6, there are two kinds of object – nests of two species of ant – but in the other examples, the objects are all of the same kind.

In the patterns of events in time discussed in Part II, each point in a pattern was called an event. Each point in a spatial pattern is called an **object**, the objects being trees, post offices, ants' nests or whatever.

The shapes and sizes of objects will not be considered here: it will be assumed that an object can be thought of as lying at a single point. The objects can be represented as points because the distances between them are generally large compared with the sizes of individual objects. In more detailed analyses of spatial patterns, the size or shape of objects could well be of importance – for example, the size of red blood cells is of the same order of magnitude as the distance between them.

In each example, the points form a pattern in space. In Figures 9.1, 9.2 and 9.4, the space is one-dimensional and the points are strung out along a straight line (representing a road in Figures 9.1 and 9.2, and a transect of a wood in Figure 9.4). In the other figures, the space is two-dimensional, and the points are positioned over a region.

From the point of view of probability modelling and statistical analysis, spatial patterns of objects along a line are essentially the same as patterns of events in time, and hence they can be studied by the methods of Part II. Accordingly, Sections 10 to 13 are concerned mainly with spatial patterns in two dimensions.

Summary of Section 9

Each point in a spatial pattern is called an object. In this section, you have seen examples of spatial patterns in which the objects lie along a line and examples in which the objects are distributed in two-dimensional space. In some of the patterns, the objects appear to be located randomly, whereas in others they are either fairly regularly positioned or clustered. A narrow strip across a two-dimensional spatial pattern is called a transect. The positions of objects in a transect, when represented as points along a straight line, form a one-dimensional spatial pattern.

10 Random patterns in space

In all the examples in Section 9, the spatial pattern occurs over continuous space so that an object can appear at any position on the given line or in the given area. Patterns in space may also occur in discrete space, though these rarely occur in practice. An example of a pattern in discrete space is the pattern that arises when trees are planted in a regular pattern, and after a period of time some of the trees have died.

Two models for objects located randomly in space are described in this section. These are the two-dimensional analogues of the Bernoulli process and the Poisson process for events in time. The two-dimensional Bernoulli process, which is a model for events in discrete space, is discussed briefly in Subsection 10.1. The two-dimensional Poisson process is introduced in Subsection 10.2, and simulation for a two-dimensional Poisson process is discussed in Subsection 10.3.

10.1 The two-dimensional Bernoulli process

A square array consisting of 20 rows each containing 20 random digits is shown in Figure 10.1(a). The 9s are ringed in this figure; there are 41 of these among the 400 digits (very close to the 40 expected).

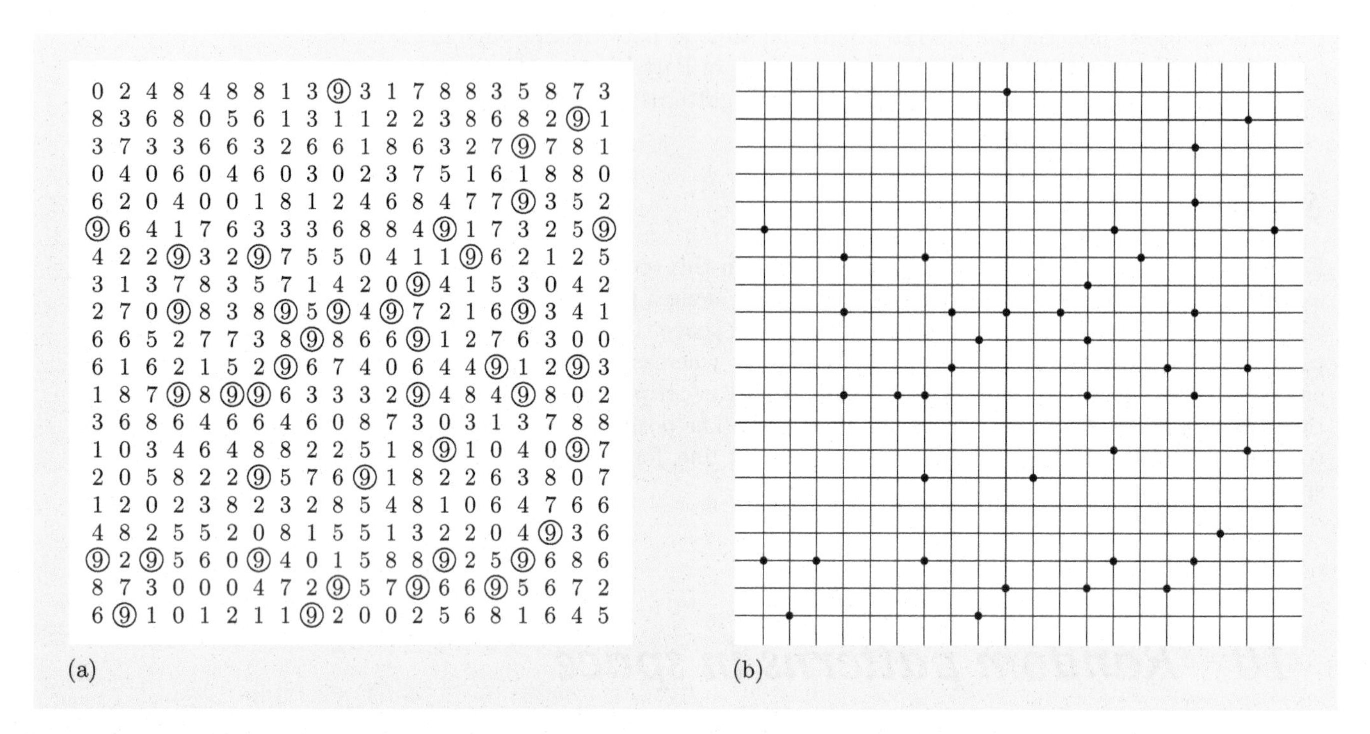

Figure 10.1 (a) A 20×20 square array of random digits (b) A random pattern in discrete space

In Figure 10.1(b), the positions of the 9s are shown on the vertices of a 20×20 **square lattice**. The word 'square' refers to the shape of the individual cells, not to the fact that the pattern in Figure 10.1(b) happens to cover a square area of 20 units $\times$ 20 units.

The positions marked in Figure 10.1(b) form a realisation of a **two-dimensional Bernoulli process**. In such a process, at each point (x, y) of the square lattice there can be either an object (with probability p) or no object (with probability $q = 1 - p$); occurrences of objects at different lattice points are independent. In the simulation that gave rise to the realisation in Figure 10.1(b), p is equal to 0.1. The two-dimensional Bernoulli process can be regarded as a random pattern in discrete space.

10.2 The two-dimensional Poisson process

The one-dimensional Poisson process is a model for events that occur at random in time in such a way that the underlying rate of occurrence of events remains constant. The two-dimensional Poisson process, which is the continuous analogue of the two-dimensional Bernoulli process, is a model for objects distributed randomly in space. It is defined in essentially the same way as the one-dimensional Poisson process. The only difference is that the three postulates are expressed in terms of small areas δa instead of short time (or length) intervals $[t, t + \delta t]$. The postulates for the two-dimensional Poisson process are stated in the following box.

Postulates for the two-dimensional Poisson process

I The probability that there is (exactly) one object in any small region of area δa is equal to $\lambda\,\delta a + o(\delta a)$.

II The probability that there are two or more objects in a small region of area δa is equal to $o(\delta a)$.

III The presence of an object in any region A_1, and the presence of an object in any non-overlapping region A_2, are independent events.

The parameter λ is called the **density** of the Poisson process. It represents the mean number of objects per unit area – for example, trees per hectare or post offices per square kilometre.

An important difference between a one-dimensional and a two-dimensional Poisson process is that in the latter there is no obvious ordering of objects (or events). In a one-dimensional process in time, events occur in a definite order and it makes sense to talk about the time between successive events or the time until six events have occurred. With a spatial pattern, all the objects are assumed to be in position at some instant in time. This difference is discussed further in Section 12.

For the one-dimensional Poisson process in time, the number of events occurring in any time interval of duration t has a Poisson distribution with parameter λt. The corresponding result for the Poisson process in two dimensions is stated in the following box.

The number of objects in a region

For a Poisson process in two-dimensional space with density λ per unit area, the number of objects in any region of area A has a Poisson distribution with parameter λA.

This result can be derived using the method that was used in Section 4 to derive the corresponding result for a one-dimensional Poisson process.

Example 10.1 Plants in a region

The positions of a particular species of plant over a large region of turf may be assumed to be reasonably modelled by a two-dimensional Poisson process with plant density $\lambda = 1.6$ per square metre. Suppose that a square section of turf with each side 1.5 metres long is cut away and removed.

The number of plants in this section of turf is a random variable N that has a Poisson distribution with parameter

$$\lambda A = 1.6 \times 1.5 \times 1.5 = 3.6.$$

Therefore the probability that there are no plants in the section of turf is

$$P(N = 0) = e^{-3.6} \simeq 0.0273.$$

The probability that there are at least three plants in the section of turf is

$$\begin{aligned} P(N \geq 3) &= 1 - P(N \leq 2) \\ &= 1 - e^{-3.6}\left(1 + 3.6 + \frac{3.6^2}{2!}\right) \\ &\simeq 1 - 0.3027 \\ &= 0.6973. \end{aligned}$$ ♦

Activity 10.1 Primroses in a clearing

Primroses grow in a clearing in a wood with a density of 1.2 plants per square metre. It may be assumed that the primroses are located randomly in the clearing.

(a) Calculate the probability that there are exactly three primroses in a square of area one square metre.

(b) Calculate the probability that there are exactly three primroses in a circle of area one square metre.

(c) Calculate the probability that there are no primroses growing in a particular area of one square metre.

(d) Calculate the probability that at least five primroses are found in an area of two square metres.

Transects across random patterns

A spatial pattern of white oak trees in a wood was described briefly in Example 9.3. A transect was marked across the region in Figure 9.3, and the one-dimensional pattern in Figure 9.4 was obtained from the oak trees in the transect. Clearly, the properties of a one-dimensional pattern along a transect are related to the two-dimensional pattern on which the transect is drawn. If the spatial pattern is random (that is, if it is a two-dimensional Poisson process), then the pattern obtained from the transect is also random (a one-dimensional Poisson process). The derivation of this result involves using the postulates of the two-dimensional Poisson process to show that the pattern along the transect satisfies the postulates for a one-dimensional Poisson process. The details will not be given here.

10.3 Simulation for Poisson processes

The positions of objects in a Poisson process in one-dimensional space can be easily simulated. Probably the simplest way to do this, as described in Subsection 3.3, is to simulate successive intervals using random numbers from an exponential distribution. However, this method cannot be extended to simulate the positions of objects in a two-dimensional Poisson process. Therefore a different method, based on the uniform distribution, will be introduced.

Suppose that it is known that in a Poisson process, exactly one object has been observed along a line AB of length a (see Figure 10.2). By the first postulate of the Poisson process, the probability that an object (event) occurs in any small interval of fixed length is the same, wherever that interval lies. It follows that the object is equally likely to be at any point P on the line, and hence the length AP has the uniform distribution $U(0, a)$.

Figure 10.2 The position of a point P along a line AB of length a

Now suppose that, instead of one object, it is known that k objects have been observed on the line AB. By the third postulate, objects occur independently of each other. So if the positions of the k objects are $P_1, P_2, \ldots, P_k$, then each of the lengths $AP_1, AP_2, \ldots, AP_k$ has the uniform distribution $U(0, a)$, and these distributions are independent.

Example 10.2 Simulating a Poisson process

The positions of objects on a line of length 40 units in a one-dimensional Poisson process with density $\lambda = 0.1$ objects per unit length will be simulated. The simulation will be carried out in two stages. First, the number of objects in the length of 40 units will be simulated, and then the positions of the objects.

The number of objects is an observed value n of a random variable N whose distribution is Poisson with parameter

$$\lambda \times \text{length} = 0.1 \times 40 = 4.$$

Given a value u from $U(0, 1)$, the simulated value n satisfies

$$F(n-1) < u \leq F(n),$$

where $F(n)$ is the c.d.f. of N. Values of the c.d.f. of $N \sim \text{Poisson}(4)$ are included in Table 10.1.

Table 10.1 The p.m.f. and c.d.f. of $N \sim \text{Poisson}(4)$

n	0	1	2	3	$\cdots$
$P(N = n)$	0.0183	0.0733	0.1465	0.1954	$\cdots$
$F(n) = P(N \leq n)$	0.0183	0.0916	0.2381	0.4335	$\cdots$

Starting (for instance) at the top of the final column of Table 5 in the *Handbook* gives 1, 3, 9, 6, so take $u = 0.1396$. Since

$$F(1) = 0.0916 < 0.1396 < 0.2381 = F(2),$$

the simulated value of N is $n = 2$. That is, there are two objects in the simulation.

The positions of two points P_1 and P_2 on the line AB, which is 40 units long, will now be simulated. Each of the lengths AP_1 and AP_2 is an observation from the uniform distribution $U(0, 40)$. Continuing down the final column of Table 5 in the *Handbook*, taking groups of three digits, gives

$$AP_1 = 0.822 \times 40 = 32.88,$$
$$AP_2 = 0.103 \times 40 = 4.12.$$

The simulated positions of the objects are illustrated in Figure 10.3.

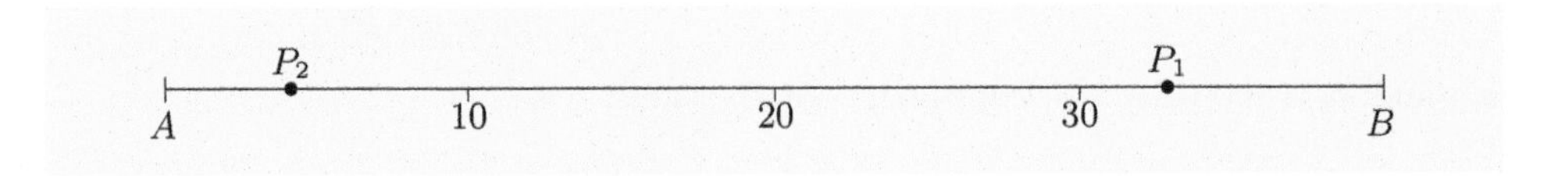

Figure 10.3 A realisation of a Poisson process with density 0.1 ♦

Activity 10.2 Another simulation

Simulate a second realisation of a Poisson process in one-dimensional space with density $\lambda = 0.1$ per unit length over a length of 40 units. Use random digits from the thirtieth row of Table 5 in the *Handbook* (beginning 23861). Draw a rough diagram showing the positions of the objects on the line.

The method used in Example 10.2 for simulating the positions of objects on a line in a Poisson process can be extended to simulate the positions of objects in a two-dimensional Poisson process: the number of objects in a region is simulated first, then the position of each object is simulated. The method is illustrated in Example 10.3.

Example 10.3 Simulating a Poisson process in two dimensions

A realisation of a two-dimensional Poisson process with density $\lambda = 0.1$ over an area of observation that is a square of 20 units by 20 units will be simulated.

The number of objects in a 20×20 square is a random variable N that has a Poisson distribution with parameter

$$\lambda A = 0.1 \times 20^2 = 40.$$

Given an observation u from $U(0,1)$, a value n of N is simulated by choosing n to satisfy $F(n-1) < u \leq F(n)$, where $F(n)$ is the c.d.f. of $N \sim \text{Poisson}(40)$. The last four digits of the bottom row of Table 5 in the *Handbook* are 1, 9, 6, 0, so let $u = 0.1960$. If you calculated values of the c.d.f. of N, you would find that $F(34) = 0.1938$ and $F(35) = 0.2423$. Since $F(34) < 0.1960 < F(35)$, a simulated value of N is $n = 35$.

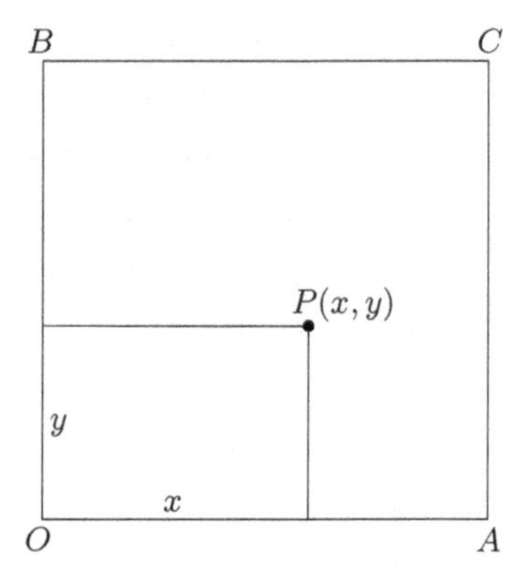

Figure 10.4 The square region $OABC$

Next, the positions of 35 objects within the 20×20 square area $OABC$ will be simulated (see Figure 10.4). The position P of any object is equally likely to be at any point in the square, so the x- and y-coordinates of P, relative to the bottom left-hand corner O of the region, are independent random values from the uniform distribution $U(0,20)$. A value from $U(0,20)$ can be obtained by taking a random observation from $U(0,1)$ and multiplying it by 20. Random values u from $U(0,1)$ will be obtained by taking groups of three digits from Table 5 in the *Handbook*, starting at the beginning of Row 36 (46300, 42305, ...) and reading across this row and the following rows.

The first two values are $u_1 = 0.463$ and $u_2 = 0.004$, so the coordinates of P_1, the position of the first object, are

$$(20u_1, 20u_2) = (20 \times 0.463, 20 \times 0.004) = (9.26, 0.08).$$

The position of the second object is independent of P_1 and is simulated in the same way. Using the next two groups of three digits from Row 36 gives the following coordinates for P_2:

$$(20 \times 0.230, 20 \times 0.567) = (4.60, 11.34).$$

This procedure is continued until the positions of 35 objects have been simulated. The coordinates of the positions of the objects in this simulation are given in Table 10.2, and the positions are plotted in Figure 10.5.

Figure 10.5 represents the required simulation of a Poisson process with density 0.1 over a square region of area 20 units $\times$ 20 units. A pattern such as that in Figure 10.5, which arises when objects are distributed according to a two-dimensional Poisson process, is called a **random pattern** or **random spatial pattern**.

Table 10.2 Positions of 35 objects

Position of object	u_1	u_2	Coordinates $(20u_1, 20u_2)$
P_1	0.463	0.004	$(9.26, 0.08)$
P_2	0.230	0.567	$(4.60, 11.34)$
P_3	0.835	0.029	$(16.70, 0.58)$
P_4	0.310	0.063	$(6.20, 1.26)$
P_5	0.562	0.453	$(11.24, 9.06)$
P_6	0.943	0.643	$(18.86, 12.86)$
P_7	0.763	0.316	$(15.26, 6.32)$
P_8	0.298	0.979	$(5.96, 19.58)$
P_9	0.790	0.946	$(15.80, 18.92)$
P_{10}	0.315	0.906	$(6.30, 18.12)$
P_{11}	0.883	0.641	$(17.66, 12.82)$
P_{12}	0.979	0.229	$(19.58, 4.58)$
P_{13}	0.648	0.255	$(12.96, 5.10)$
P_{14}	0.008	0.069	$(0.16, 1.38)$
P_{15}	0.677	0.989	$(13.54, 19.78)$
P_{16}	0.994	0.780	$(19.88, 15.60)$
P_{17}	0.712	0.175	$(14.24, 3.50)$
P_{18}	0.293	0.535	$(5.86, 10.70)$
P_{19}	0.843	0.152	$(16.86, 3.04)$
P_{20}	0.009	0.270	$(0.18, 5.40)$
P_{21}	0.406	0.007	$(8.12, 0.14)$
P_{22}	0.388	0.718	$(7.76, 14.36)$
P_{23}	0.462	0.356	$(9.24, 7.12)$
P_{24}	0.014	0.028	$(0.28, 0.56)$
P_{25}	0.038	0.026	$(0.76, 0.52)$
P_{26}	0.829	0.227	$(16.58, 4.54)$
P_{27}	0.121	0.865	$(2.42, 17.30)$
P_{28}	0.095	0.319	$(1.90, 6.38)$
P_{29}	0.498	0.613	$(9.96, 12.26)$
P_{30}	0.543	0.612	$(10.86, 12.24)$
P_{31}	0.856	0.406	$(17.12, 8.12)$
P_{32}	0.233	0.759	$(4.66, 15.18)$
P_{33}	0.624	0.820	$(12.48, 16.40)$
P_{34}	0.020	0.421	$(0.40, 8.42)$
P_{35}	0.063	0.806	$(1.26, 16.12)$

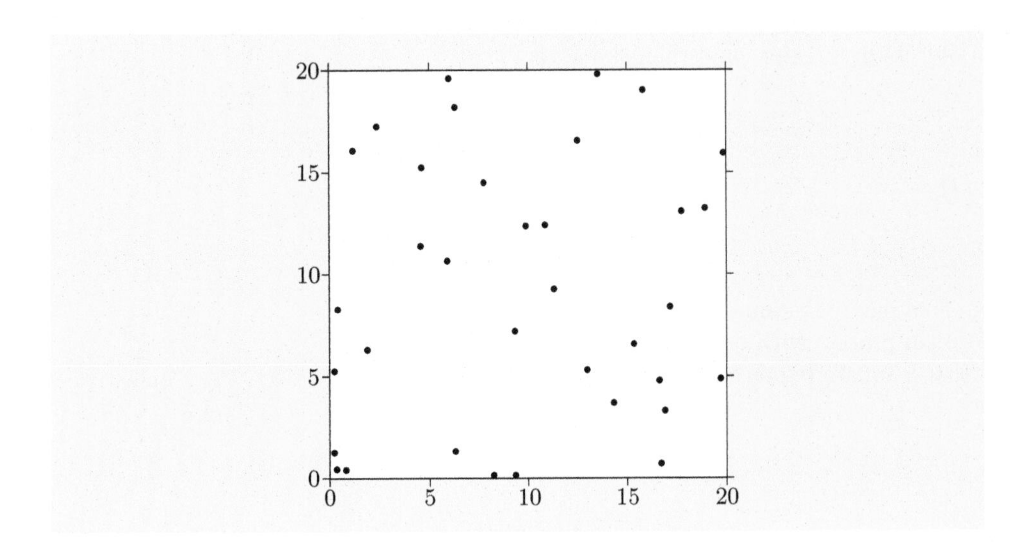

Figure 10.5 A simulation of a two-dimensional Poisson process ◆

Example 10.4 A random pattern on a rectangle

The method used in Example 10.3 can also be used to generate a simulation of a random pattern on a rectangle of size $a \times b$. The number of objects is determined by simulating an observation from a Poisson distribution with parameter λab. The positions are simulated by taking random observations from $U(0,1)$ in pairs, multiplying one by a and the other by b. ♦

Activity 10.3 Simulating the positions of primroses

Primroses growing in a clearing in a wood may be assumed to be randomly located according to a Poisson process with density $\lambda = 1.2$ plants per square metre (as in Activity 10.1).

Simulate the positions of plants in a rectangular section of the clearing that is 2.5 metres wide and 1.6 metres long. Use random digits from Row 16 of Table 5 in the *Handbook* (beginning 14712). Draw a rough sketch showing the positions of the plants.

Activity 10.4 Simulating a Poisson process over an irregular area

Explain how you would simulate a random pattern with a given density over an irregular area such as a map of the United Kingdom.

Summary of Section 10

Two models for random patterns in two-dimensional space have been described in this section – the Bernoulli process, which is a model for a random pattern in discrete space, and the Poisson process, which is a model for a random pattern in continuous space. These models are extensions of the models for events in time introduced in Parts I and II. The main result given for a two-dimensional Poisson process with density λ per unit area concerns the number of objects in a region of area A: the number of objects has a Poisson distribution with parameter λA. You have seen that a realisation of a two-dimensional Poisson process can be simulated by first simulating the number of objects in a region, and then simulating the position of each object.

The Bernoulli process is discussed in Subsection 1.2, and the Poisson process in Sections 3 and 4.

Exercises on Section 10

Exercise 10.1 Objects in a square region

The positions of objects in a large area may be assumed to be reasonably modelled by a two-dimensional Poisson process with density $\lambda = 20$ per square metre. Calculate the probability that a square region with sides 30 centimetres long contains exactly three objects.

Exercise 10.2 Objects in a rectangular region

The positions of objects in a large area may be assumed to be reasonably modelled by a two-dimensional Poisson process with density $\lambda = 2.4 \times 10^{-3}$ per square metre. Calculate the probability that a rectangular region 20 metres wide and 30 metres long contains more than two objects.

Exercise 10.3 Simulation

The positions of objects in a large area may be assumed to be reasonably modelled by a two-dimensional Poisson process with density $\lambda = 2.5 \times 10^{-4}$ per square metre. Part of the area is divided into cordoned rectangular regions, each 100 metres wide and 80 metres long.

(a) What is the probability distribution of the number of objects in a cordoned region?

(b) Use the number 0.6831, which is a random observation from the uniform distribution $U(0, 1)$, to simulate the number of objects in a cordoned region.

(c) Explain briefly, without carrying out the simulation, how you would simulate the positions of the objects in the region in part (b).

11 Non-random spatial patterns

Patterns with regularity and patterns with clustering are the two main types of spatial pattern that are not random. Some models for these types of pattern are described briefly in this section.

11.1 Patterns with regularity

There are many spatial patterns in which the objects are more uniformly positioned than in a random pattern, and these are known as **patterns with regularity**. They arise in a variety of situations that lead to different kinds of regularity, and hence different models are required. In Figure 9.7, the pattern of *Messor* ants' nests shows too much regularity to be regarded as random; the likely reason for this is that each nest has its own foraging territory, so that there is a tendency for the inhabited area to be shared out between the nests. The London post offices shown in Figure 9.5 also appear to have a fairly regular pattern. This is due to human planning. If post offices were sited according to a two-dimensional Poisson process, then sometimes two post offices would be positioned very close to each other, and this would obviously not be sensible. The ants' nests and the post offices both occur in patterns with regularity for similar reasons. There are also other types of situation that give rise to patterns with regularity. Some of these are discussed later in this subsection.

The extreme case is that of complete regularity, when the objects are laid out exactly in a uniform pattern. In one dimension, this simply means that the objects are uniformly spaced; for example, the ten hurdles in a 110-metre race are positioned with exactly 9.14 metres between successive hurdles. In two dimensions, the objects occur at the vertices of a **lattice** that is built up of regular polygons. The most obvious form of lattice is the **square lattice** (see Figure 11.1(a)), which can be thought of as being constructed by fitting together equal-sized squares. There are only two other possible regular lattice patterns – the **triangular lattice** (Figure 11.1(b)), which is made up of equilateral triangles, and the **hexagonal lattice** (Figure 11.1(c)), which is composed of regular hexagons.

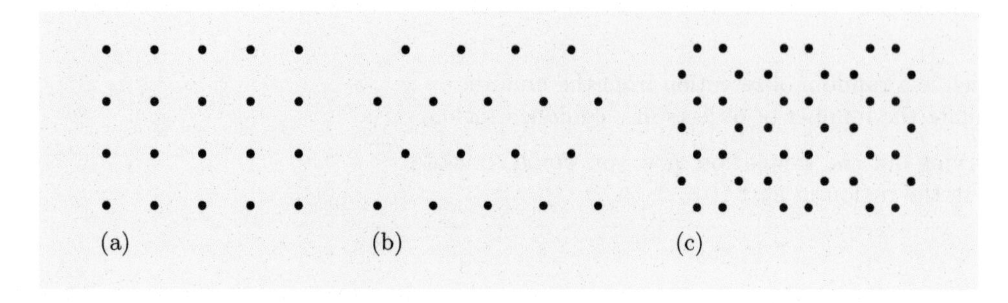

Figure 11.1 The three regular lattice patterns

Trees planted in an orchard and plants in a nursery provide familiar examples of completely regular patterns; square and triangular lattices are the most common.

Now suppose, for example, that bushes are meant to be planted according to a plan that positions them at the vertices $V_1, V_2, \ldots$ of (say) a square lattice. In practice, they may be positioned not exactly at $V_1, V_2, \ldots$, but instead at positions $P_1, P_2, \ldots$ slightly displaced from $V_1, V_2, \ldots$. This is illustrated in Figure 11.2.

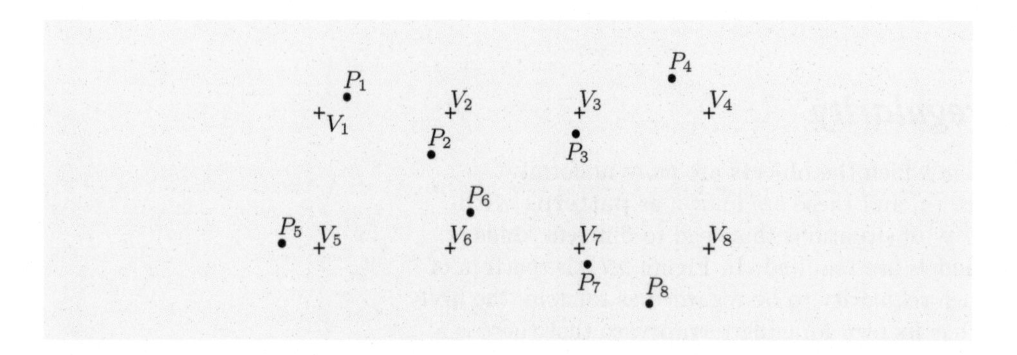

Figure 11.2 A lattice pattern with independent random displacements

The pattern of bush positions will not be *completely* regular, but it will be much more regular than a random pattern. This is an example of a pattern possessing regularity, but not complete regularity.

To model such a pattern, it is necessary to model the displacements $V_1P_1, V_2P_2, \ldots$ as regards both their *magnitudes* and their *directions*. A natural assumption might be that the directions are independent and uniformly distributed from 0 to 2π, and that the magnitudes (that is, the lengths $V_1P_1, V_2P_2, \ldots$) are independent of each other and of the directions, and have some common distribution. This type of pattern is called a **lattice pattern with independent random displacements**.

Another regular pattern that can arise in the orchard or plantation context is when the trees were indeed planted in a lattice formation, but some of them have subsequently died. One modelling assumption might be that death occurs independently from tree to tree among those originally planted, with a small probability p of occurrence, and that p is the same for each original tree. This pattern is a **lattice pattern with random deaths**.

Activity 11.1 A lattice pattern with random deaths

Suppose that the trees in an orchard were originally planted at the vertices of a square lattice, and that deaths of trees occur randomly as in a lattice pattern with random deaths. What other name is given to the spatial pattern of the surviving trees?

Activity 11.2 Is the model satisfactory?

Suppose that trees are planted in a lattice formation in an orchard, and that some years later, 5% of them have died. Explain why a lattice pattern with random deaths might be unsatisfactory as a model for the pattern of surviving trees.

The models that have been developed so far for patterns with regularity are modifications of completely regular lattice patterns. Models for patterns with regularity can also be developed in other ways. One of the most important causes of regularity is **inhibition** between objects that are near to one another: it is sometimes physically impossible for two objects in close proximity to coexist. For example, two trees cannot grow very close to each other. This property of inhibition provides the basis of a model known as a **sequential inhibition process**.

Suppose, for example, that plants grow in chronological succession from seeds randomly scattered by wind or other agencies. If all the seeds were to produce viable plants, these would be positioned over the area in a random pattern. In a two-dimensional Poisson process, objects can be very close to each other. However, in reality, a new plant may well be unable to survive if too near to plants already growing. When this is so, the loss of plants that are inhibitively near to other plants produces an element of regularity in the spatial pattern. This is the model for a sequential inhibition process.

The reason for the name of the model is now apparent. It is *sequential* because objects are added one at a time to the pattern, and it has *inhibition* because an object is prevented or inhibited from belonging to the pattern if there is another object too near to it.

Suppose that the minimum distance permitted between objects in a sequential inhibition process is d, and that if the distance between a new object and an existing object is greater than d, then the new object is added to the pattern. In this case, the model is known as a **simple sequential inhibition process**.

The word *simple* in the title of the simple sequential inhibition process reflects the all-or-nothing nature of the minimum separation condition as it is applied in this process. Placing two objects at a separation of less than d is impossible; but placing them at a separation greater than d, even if not much greater than d, is unrestricted.

In many practical situations, however, inhibition operates in a less cut-and-dried way. If a bush is planted at distance r units from an existing bush, the new bush might be certain to die if r is too small (say $r \leq r_1$) and certain to survive if r is sufficiently large (say $r \geq r_2$); for intermediate values of the separation ($r_1 < r < r_2$), survival might be a matter of chance. This situation could be modelled by specifying as a function of r the probability $p(r)$ that the new bush survives: $p(r) = 0$ for $r \leq r_1$, $p(r)$ increases from 0 to 1 in some specified way as r increases from r_1 to r_2, and $p(r) = 1$ for $r \geq r_2$. A typical form of the function $p(r)$ is shown in Figure 11.3(a). In the simple sequential inhibition process, $r_1 = r_2 = d$ and $p(r)$ is a step function, as shown in Figure 11.3(b).

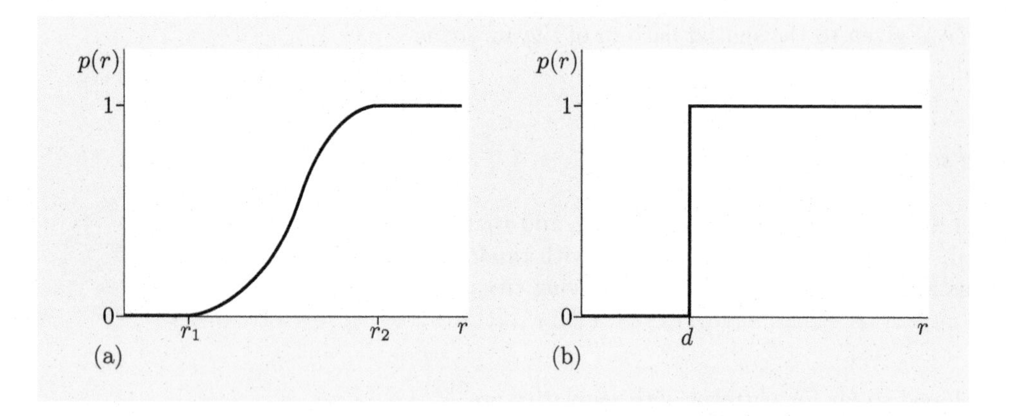

Figure 11.3 Functions specifying the probability that a new bush survives

In a sequential inhibition process, the pattern is built up object by object, sequentially. This is actually a random process in both space and time. The spatial pattern changes with time. However, most of the spatial patterns in this book are assumed to be fixed throughout time, and time is not an essential feature of a process with inhibition. Suppose, for example, that seeds are randomly scattered by the wind in autumn and germinate the following spring. If two of the seeds fall close together, only one will be able to develop into an adult plant, and the other will die. To model this pattern, if two objects in a two-dimensional Poisson process are less than some distance d apart, one of the objects is eliminated (selected by a random procedure). The model needs to be specified carefully when there are three or more objects close together.

11.2 Patterns with clustering

Models for spatial patterns in which objects are more likely to occur closer together than they would be in a random pattern, so that there is a tendency for them to appear in groups or **clusters**, are discussed briefly in this subsection. Such patterns are known as **patterns with clustering**. The redwood seedlings in region II of Figure 9.6 provide an example of a clustered pattern.

Clustering may arise for various reasons. In a botanical context, there are two well-recognised causes of clustering of plants. These are described in an article by E.C. Pielou:

> On the one hand seeds may fall at random over an area but if the habitat is not homogeneous the proportion germinating and thriving will vary from site to site so that the density is high in some sites and low in others. On the other hand the habitat may be homogeneous but the individual plants may occur in family groups owing to the fact that they reproduce vegetatively or by seeds with small radius of dispersal.

Pielou, E.C. (1960) 'A single mechanism to account for regular, random and aggregated populations', *Journal of Ecology*, vol. 48, no. 3, pp. 575–84.

Pielou calls these two causes of clustered patterns **heterogeneity of habitat** and **reproductive clumping**, respectively.

Clustered patterns also arise in other contexts, such as human geography and animal behaviour. Towns on a map of the United Kingdom occur in clusters. This is because towns develop in suitable locations such as by rivers, and not in very mountainous country. This resembles the botanical situation of heterogeneity of habitat. If the spatially distributed objects are, for example, herbivorous animals such as cows or kangaroos grazing freely over a large area, they graze not as isolated individuals but 'socially' in a number of groups. Again, if the objects are retail shops of all kinds in the suburban regions of a city, these will tend to be clustered together in various main and subsidiary shopping centres. In these situations there is association between the individuals (shops, kangaroos or whatever) belonging to the same cluster. This resembles the botanical situation of reproductive clumping. In three dimensions, stars occur not randomly in space but in clusters or galaxies.

Heterogeneity of habitat: models for patterns with clusters

Non-homogeneous Poisson processes for modelling events in time were described in Section 6. They are Poisson processes in which the rate of occurrence of events is a known function of time, $\lambda(t)$. This sort of model can also apply in two dimensions, so that the density of objects is a function of position. This would be appropriate for a model of seeds germinating over an area if it were possible to specify how the fertility of the land varied; for example, it might increase from north to south and also from east to west. Then at places of high fertility, the value of the density, λ, is high, so there will tend to be more objects occurring in the Poisson process, and this will lead to a cluster of points.

Reproductive clumping: models for patterns with clusters

The models that are described below are two-dimensional analogues of the model described in Section 7 for a compound Poisson process, in which compound events occur according to a Poisson process, and multiple occurrences of some other event are associated with each compound event. In the two-dimensional analogue, objects are clustered around some point.

Consider a pattern composed of clusters of objects that are in some way dependent on each other. Each cluster may be a group of cows grazing together or a number of plants that have reproduced vegetatively from a parent plant. In each cluster there is assumed to be a cluster centre that, in this model, is not itself the position of an object but only a geometrical point. This pattern is modelled by assuming that the cluster centres are distributed according to a two-dimensional Poisson process. The number of objects located around each cluster centre is a random variable Y that is discrete and positive, for there must be at least one object in each cluster. The positions of the objects in each cluster are usually randomly displaced from the cluster centre. Both the distance from the cluster centre and the direction are random variables. This general model is called a **randomly-positioned clusters model.**

The clusters are the same as the 'family groups' in the above quotation from E.C. Pielou.

This model can be formulated in a slightly different way so that each cluster centre is itself the position of an object. This is essentially the same model as the previous one; the way in which it is formulated reflects situations when the cluster centre (head office, plant) is in some sense a parent, and the cluster (branch offices, plants formed by vegetative reproduction) comprises offspring.

Activity 11.3 Choosing a model

For each of the following 'objects' located in two-dimensional space, suggest a model for their disposition that you consider to be more suitable than a two-dimensional Poisson process. Explain why you have chosen your model in each case.

(a) People in a sparsely populated area

(b) Farmhouses in a rural area

Summary of Section 11

Some probability models for patterns with regularity and patterns with clustering have been described briefly in this section. Patterns with regularity arise when objects lie very close together so that they tend to be fairly regularly spaced. Models for such patterns include sequential inhibition processes and lattice patterns with random deaths or independent random displacements. Two models for patterns with clustering are the two-dimensional non-homogeneous Poisson process, which is appropriate when clustering is due to heterogeneity of habitat, and the randomly-positioned clusters model, which is suitable for modelling clustered patterns caused by reproductive clumping.

12 Counts and distances

The two main features of interest in a point process are the number of events that occur in a fixed time interval, and the time that elapses between successive events. When discussing a spatial process of objects along a line as in Figure 9.1 or Figure 9.4, instead of a process of events in time, the language needs to be adjusted. The features of interest now are the number or **count** of objects that lie in a given interval along the line, and the **distance** between neighbouring objects. Note, however, that there is an essential difference between the patterns of events in time and those in a one-dimensional spatial pattern. In time, there is a definite ordering so that one event follows another: the 'next' event is unambiguous. However, in space, there are two objects 'next' to each object – one on each side.

Counts and distances in one dimension are illustrated in Figure 12.1.

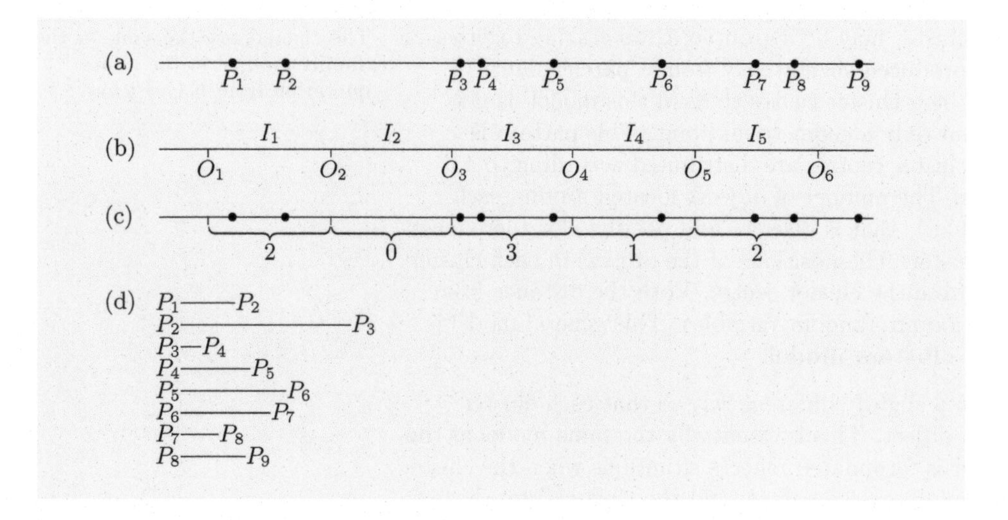

Figure 12.1 Counts and distances in one dimension

A pattern of points $P_1, P_2, \ldots$, which are the positions of objects along a line, is shown in Figure 12.1(a). As a reference framework, a grid of points $O_1, O_2, \ldots$ can be marked on the line, as in Figure 12.1(b). This grid divides the line into equal intervals $O_1O_2, O_2O_3, \ldots$, labelled $I_1, I_2, \ldots$. The pattern can be studied either in terms of the counts of objects in the grid intervals $I_1, I_2, \ldots$, as shown in Figure 12.1(c), or in terms of the distances between neighbouring objects, $P_1P_2, P_2P_3, \ldots$, as shown in Figure 12.1(d).

Do these ideas about counts and distances still apply for spatial patterns in two dimensions? The extension of counts to patterns in two dimensions is the subject of Subsection 12.1. Distances and their properties are discussed in Subsection 12.2.

12.1 Counts of objects and their properties

The simulated pattern of 35 objects in Figure 10.5 will be used to illustrate some ideas about counts of objects for two-dimensional spatial patterns.

In the one-dimensional case, a linear grid is superposed on the pattern. This grid divides the line into equal intervals. In two dimensions, a square grid is superposed on the pattern. This grid divides the surveyed area into equal squares or **quadrats**. Each quadrat has the same area.

Figure 12.2 shows the spatial pattern of Figure 10.5 with a grid of quadrats superposed on it.

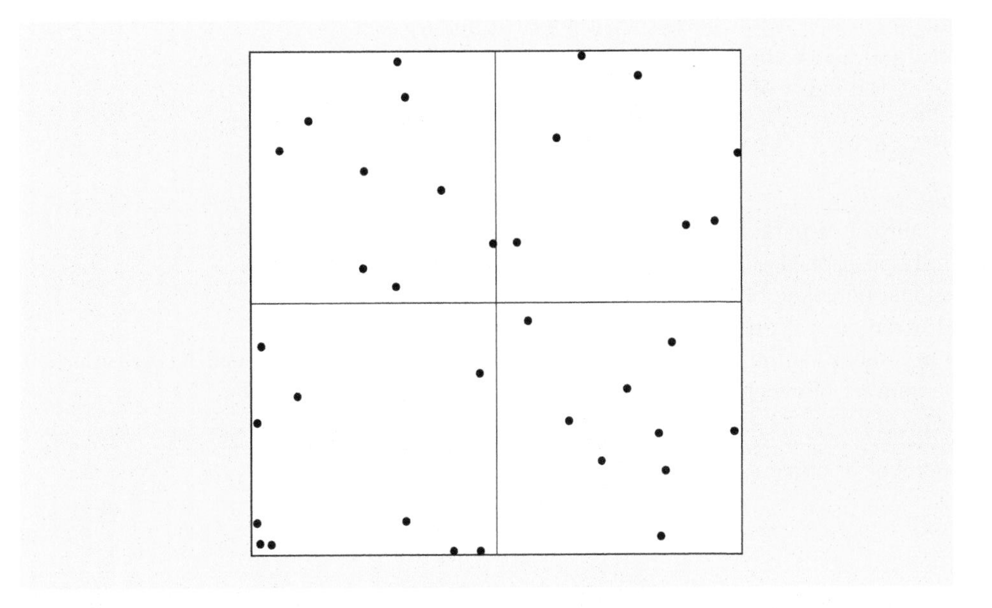

Figure 12.2 A random spatial pattern with a superposed grid

9	7
10	9

Figure 12.3 Counts of objects in quadrats

The counts of objects in the quadrats are shown in Figure 12.3. These counts can be used to gain an insight into the nature of the pattern. One method of doing this involves the *index of dispersion* for a spatial pattern. This is defined as follows.

Suppose that a region of area A is marked out in the plane inhabited by objects in a spatial pattern; this region could be a square quadrat or have some other shape. The number of objects in the pattern falling in the region is a random variable X. The **index of dispersion** for the spatial pattern, denoted I, is the ratio of the variance of X to its mean:

The index of dispersion for a point process was defined in Section 8.

$$I = \frac{V(X)}{E(X)}. \qquad (12.1)$$

Random patterns

For a two-dimensional Poisson process with density λ, X, the number of objects in a region of area A, has a Poisson distribution with parameter λA. Therefore the mean and variance of X are both equal to λA, and hence the index of dispersion is 1.

The distribution of X was discussed in Subsection 10.2.

Patterns with regularity

The extreme case of a pattern with regularity is a completely regular pattern, when the objects are positioned in a lattice (triangular, square or hexagonal). Since there is no random element in their specification, and repeated realisations of the process produce exactly the same positions, the count of objects in any quadrat is a fixed quantity, and its variance is 0. Hence the index of dispersion is 0.

There might be some slight variation in the counts if, for instance, a grid of square quadrats was placed over a triangular lattice. But there is zero dispersion: the estimation procedure is a little inaccurate.

Activity 12.1 The two-dimensional Bernoulli process

Suppose that a spatial pattern consists of a two-dimensional Bernoulli process where the probability that an object is placed at any lattice point is p. Calculate the index of dispersion using rectangular quadrats of size $a \times b$.

In Activity 12.1, you found that the index of dispersion for a two-dimensional Bernoulli process is $1 - p$, which is less than 1. As p increases, the index decreases towards zero. This is what you might expect: if p is close to 1, there will be an object at most of the lattice points, and hence the pattern will show regularity and very little dispersion. In general, the index of dispersion is less than 1 for patterns with regularity.

Patterns with clustering

For patterns with clustering, the index of dispersion is generally greater than 1. Consider, for instance, the randomly-positioned clusters model. As mentioned in Section 11, this is the two-dimensional analogue of the compound Poisson process for events in time. The mean and variance of X, the number of objects in a region of area A, can be found using an argument similar to that used in Section 7 to find the mean and variance of the number of events in an interval of length t in a compound Poisson process.

The details of the derivation will be omitted.

If the mean and variance of the number of objects in a cluster are μ and σ^2, respectively, then

$$E(X) = \mu\lambda A,$$
$$V(X) = \lambda A(\sigma^2 + \mu^2),$$

where λ is the density of cluster centres. Hence the index of dispersion is given by

$$I = \frac{V(X)}{E(X)} = \frac{\sigma^2}{\mu} + \mu.$$

Since each cluster must contain at least one object, $\mu \geq 1$. It follows that, for this clustered pattern, the index of dispersion is always at least 1. It can be equal to 1 only when $\mu = 1$ and $\sigma^2 = 0$, in which case the clusters are all of size one and the pattern reduces to a two-dimensional Poisson process. The larger σ^2, the larger the value of the index of dispersion: if there is a lot of variation between cluster sizes, then there is a lot of dispersion in the total number of objects in an area.

In general, if $I < 1$ for a spatial pattern, then there is less dispersion than for a random pattern, which indicates more regularity in the pattern. If $I > 1$, then there is more dispersion or scattering of the points, which suggests some clustering. The index of dispersion and its properties can be used to develop a test for the randomness of spatial patterns. One such test is described in Section 13.

12.2 Object-to-object and point-to-object distances

In Figure 12.1(a), P_2 is consecutive to P_1, P_1P_2 is the distance between them, and the pattern of line objects gives eight such distances $P_1P_2, \ldots, P_8P_9$ from the first object, P_1, to the last one, P_9 (or, possibly, the first object, P_9, to the last one, P_1). But there is no first or last object among a pattern of objects in a plane. Thus there is no direct extension from one to two dimensions for distances.

To be precise, P_i is the position of the ith object. From now on, for simplicity, P_i will be used to represent both the object and its position.

It is, however, possible to define two types of distance measurement that give information about the nature of the spatial pattern. These are the **object-to-nearest-object distance**, denoted S, and the **point-to-nearest-object distance**, denoted R. The spatial pattern of Figure 10.5, which is reproduced in Figure 12.4 with the positions of the objects labelled, will be used to illustrate these distances.

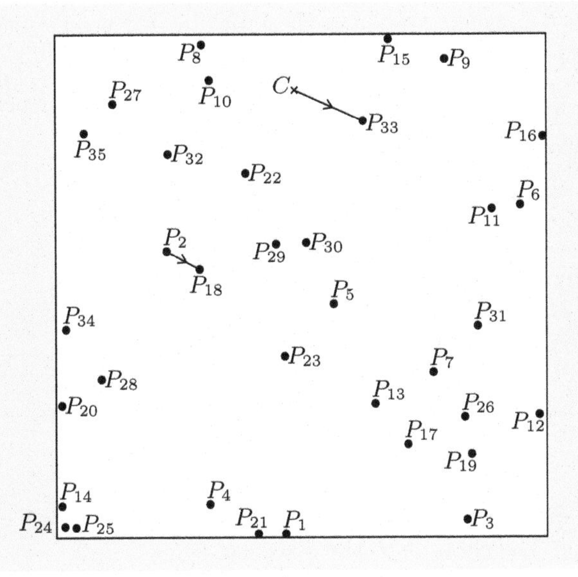

Figure 12.4 A random pattern

Since this pattern was generated sequentially, there is actually an ordering of these objects. This is ignored when calculating values of R and S.

For each object in a pattern, the value of the object-to-nearest-object distance S is the distance between the object and the object nearest to it. For example, the object nearest to P_2 is P_{18}. The distance between P_2 and P_{18} can be calculated using the coordinates given in Table 10.2. Since P_2 has coordinates $(4.60, 11.34)$ and P_{18} is $(5.86, 10.70)$, this distance is

$$P_2P_{18} = \sqrt{(4.60 - 5.86)^2 + (11.34 - 10.70)^2} \simeq 1.41.$$

This is the value of S for P_2.

Since the pattern in Figure 12.4 contains 35 objects, it could provide 35 S-values. However, it would be unreliable to measure the distance from an object close to the boundary to the nearest object within the area; for example, there could well be an object outside the boundary that is closer to P_{16} than is P_6.

Activity 12.2 Object-to-nearest-object distances

(a) In Figure 12.4, the object nearest to P_2 is P_{18}. This is indicated on the diagram by the arrow on the line joining P_2 to P_{18}. Which object is nearest to P_{18}? What is the value of S for P_{18}?

(b) If P_j is the object nearest to P_i in a spatial pattern, is P_i necessarily the object nearest to P_j? If yes, then explain why; if no, then give a counterexample from Figure 12.4.

In general, given a spatial pattern, a sample of values of S, or **S-distances** as they are sometimes called, is obtained by choosing a sample of objects at random from the objects in the pattern and calculating the value of S for each object chosen.

To obtain a value of R, the point-to-nearest-object distance, a point is chosen at random, and then the distance from that point to the nearest object is calculated. For example, suppose that the randomly chosen point is the point C marked in Figure 12.4, which has coordinates $(9.68, 17.62)$. The nearest object to C is P_{33}, which has coordinates $(12.48, 16.40)$. Therefore the observed value of R, which is called an ***R*-distance**, is

By 'point' is meant a geometrical point. With probability 1, this will not be the position of any object.

$$CP_{33} = \sqrt{(9.68 - 12.48)^2 + (17.62 - 16.40)^2} \simeq 3.05.$$

Different types of spatial pattern give rise to different types of distribution for the random variables S and R. The distributions of R and S in a random pattern, or two-dimensional Poisson process, will be discussed first. Then some general remarks will be made about the distributions of R and S for clustered and regular patterns.

The point-to-nearest-object distance R

Suppose that objects are distributed as in a two-dimensional Poisson process with density λ, and that C is a randomly-chosen point. The c.d.f. of R, the distance from C to the nearest object, is given by

$$F(r) = P(R \leq r) = 1 - P(R > r).$$

However, $P(R > r)$ is the probability that the distance from C to the nearest object is greater than r, which is the same as the probability that the object nearest to C falls outside a circle with centre C and radius r (see Figure 12.5).

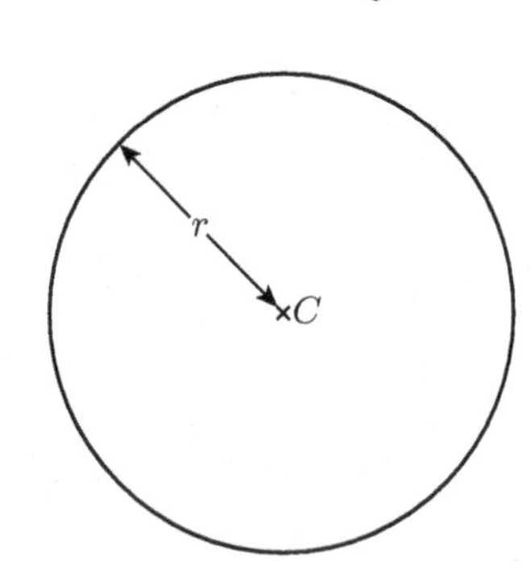

Figure 12.5 The object nearest to C falls outside the circle

If N is the number of objects in the random pattern that lie inside the circle, then N has a Poisson distribution with parameter

$$\lambda \times \text{area of circle} = \lambda \times \pi r^2 = \pi\lambda r^2.$$

That is,

$$N \sim \text{Poisson}(\pi\lambda r^2).$$

The object nearest to C lies outside the circle if and only if there are no objects within the circle, so

$$P(R > r) = P(N = 0) = e^{-\pi\lambda r^2}.$$

Hence the c.d.f. of R is given by

$$F(r) = 1 - e^{-\pi\lambda r^2}.$$

Differentiating $F(r)$ gives $f(r)$, the p.d.f. of R:

$$f(r) = 2\pi\lambda r e^{-\pi\lambda r^2}.$$

The distribution defined by the c.d.f. and p.d.f. above is an important standard distribution, called the **Rayleigh distribution**. Before discussing the Rayleigh distribution and its properties, the distribution of the object-to-nearest-object distance S will be obtained.

The object-to-nearest-object distance S

Postulate III for the two-dimensional Poisson process states that the occurrences of objects in non-overlapping areas are independent events. Therefore if an object is chosen at random and a circle is drawn with this object as centre, then the distribution of the number of objects *other than the chosen one* inside the circle does not depend on the fact that there is an object at the centre. It follows that exactly the same argument can be used to find the distribution of S as was used to find the distribution of R, and hence R and S have the same distribution. This result is stated in the following box.

The distributions of R and S for random patterns

For the two-dimensional Poisson process with density λ, the point-to-nearest-object distance R, and the object-to-nearest-object distance S, both have a Rayleigh distribution with c.d.f.

$$F(x) = 1 - e^{-\pi\lambda x^2}, \quad x > 0, \tag{12.2}$$

and p.d.f.

$$f(x) = 2\pi\lambda x e^{-\pi\lambda x^2}, \quad x > 0. \tag{12.3}$$

The Rayleigh distribution

A random variable X with the c.d.f. in (12.2) and p.d.f. in (12.3) has a Rayleigh distribution. This distribution involves one parameter, which is a scale parameter. A sketch of the p.d.f. of the distribution is shown in Figure 12.6.

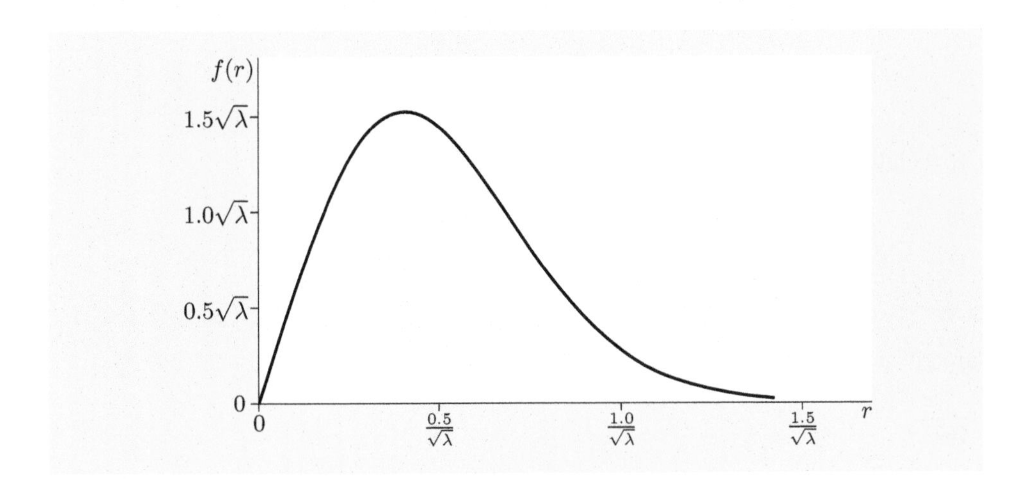

Figure 12.6 The p.d.f. of the Rayleigh distribution

Since X cannot take negative values, its mean can be found using the alternative formula for the mean:

$$E(X) = \int_0^\infty (1 - F(x))\, dx.$$

Hence

$$E(X) = \int_0^\infty e^{-\pi\lambda x^2}\, dx.$$

Since the graph of the function $e^{-\pi\lambda x^2}$ is symmetric about the vertical axis,

$$E(X) = \tfrac{1}{2}\int_{-\infty}^{\infty} e^{-\pi\lambda x^2}\,dx.$$

This integral can be evaluated using the following standard result: for $\alpha > 0$,

$$\int_{-\infty}^{\infty} e^{-\alpha w^2}\,dw = \sqrt{\frac{\pi}{\alpha}}.$$

This result is in the *Handbook.*

Using this result with $\alpha = \pi\lambda$ gives

$$E(X) = \tfrac{1}{2}\sqrt{\frac{\pi}{\pi\lambda}} = \frac{0.5}{\sqrt{\lambda}}. \qquad (12.4)$$

Activity 12.3 The median

Find the median of the Rayleigh distribution, and compare it with the mean.

Activity 12.4 The variance and the standard deviation

Show that the variance of the Rayleigh distribution is given by

$$V(X) = \frac{4-\pi}{4\pi\lambda},$$

and hence find the standard deviation.

The Rayleigh distribution and its main properties are summarised in the following box.

Rayleigh distribution

The random variable X has a Rayleigh distribution if it has c.d.f.

$$F(x) = 1 - e^{-\pi\lambda x^2}, \quad x > 0,$$

and p.d.f.

$$f(x) = 2\pi\lambda x e^{-\pi\lambda x^2}, \quad x > 0.$$

The mean and variance of X are given by

$$E(X) = \frac{0.5}{\sqrt{\lambda}}, \quad V(X) = \frac{4-\pi}{4\pi\lambda}.$$

Activity 12.5 will give you some practice at using the Rayleigh distribution to answer questions about objects distributed as in a two-dimensional Poisson process.

Activity 12.5 Objects in a random pattern

The positions of objects in a large area may be assumed to be reasonably modelled by a two-dimensional Poisson process with density 60 per square kilometre.

(a) Find the expected distance from a randomly chosen object to the object nearest to it. Calculate the probability that the nearest object is more than 100 metres away.

(b) Find the mean distance from a randomly selected point to the object nearest to it. Calculate the probability that the distance from a randomly selected point to the object nearest to it is less than 50 metres.

Clustered and regular patterns

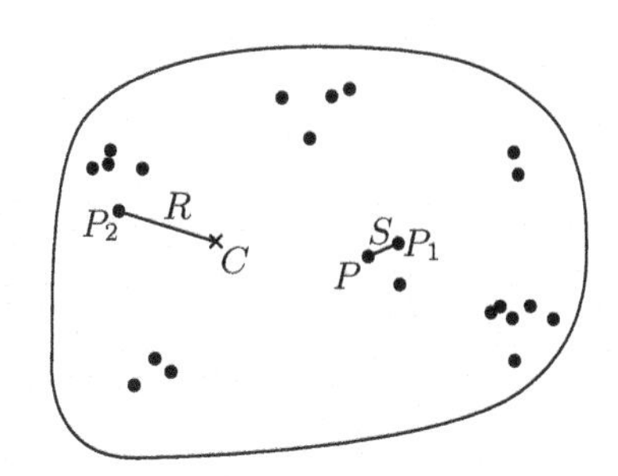

Figure 12.7 A clustered pattern

First, consider a clustered pattern such as the one in Figure 12.7. For simplicity, the pattern has been drawn so that it consists of non-overlapping clusters of objects with the clusters widely separated, so that much of the surveyed area consists of 'empty space' between the clusters.

An S-distance is measured from a randomly-chosen object, P say, to the object nearest to it. If the nearest object is labelled P_1, as illustrated in Figure 12.7, then $S = PP_1$. In general, provided that there are at least two objects in any cluster, P_1 will be in the same cluster as P. Therefore S-distances will tend to be small.

An R-distance is measured from a randomly-chosen point, C say, to the nearest object. If this object is labelled P_2 (as in Figure 12.7), then $R = CP_2$. Most points C fall in the empty space between the clusters, giving R-values that tend to be large. Thus the majority of R-values will exceed the majority of S-values.

This is true for all patterns with clustering, even if they do not consist of clearly separated clusters as in Figure 12.7. In general, the less pronounced the clusters, the less difference there will be between the average R-value and the average S-value.

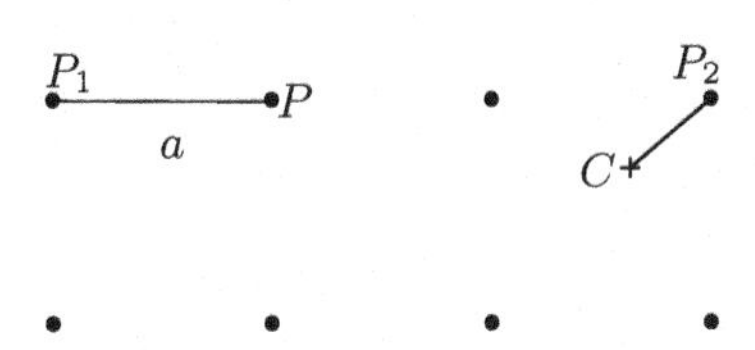

Figure 12.8 A completely regular pattern

You have seen that for a clustered pattern, R-values tend to exceed S-values, and for a random pattern, R-values and S-values have the same distribution. This suggests that for a regular pattern, R-values will tend to be less than S-values. To appreciate that this is indeed the case, consider a completely regular square lattice pattern with squares of side a, as shown in Figure 12.8. Since the pattern is completely regular, every object-to-nearest-object distance is equal to a. The point-to-nearest-object distance R is a maximum when the random point C is at the centre of a square. In this case, $R = a/\sqrt{2} \simeq 0.71a$. So R is always considerably less than S.

The difference between the average R-value and the average S-value is less marked when the pattern is not completely regular. However, there is always a tendency for R-values to be smaller than S-values. For example, for both a lattice pattern with independent random displacements and an inhibition process, objects do not occur very close to each other, so S-distances cannot be very small. On the other hand, a randomly-chosen point may be anywhere in the plane, so some R-values will be very small.

The main properties of R-distances and S-distances for different types of spatial pattern are summarised in the following box.

Properties of R-distances and S-distances

- For a random pattern, the distributions of R and S are the same. Both are Rayleigh distributions.
- For a clustered pattern, R-distances tend to be larger than S-distances.
- For a pattern with regularity, R-distances tend to be smaller than S-distances.

These properties of R-distances and S-distances can be used to investigate whether a given spatial pattern is random. A test based on comparing samples of R-distances and S-distances is described in Section 13.

Summary of Section 12

Counts and distances for two-dimensional spatial patterns have been discussed in this section. The index of dispersion for a spatial pattern has been defined; this is a measure based on the number or count of objects in a region. You have seen that the index of dispersion is equal to 1 for a random pattern, and that, in general, it is greater than 1 for clustered patterns and less than 1 for patterns with regularity. Two distances have been defined – the point-to-nearest-object distance R, and the object-to-nearest-object distance S. For a random pattern, R and S have the same Rayleigh distribution. For clustered patterns, R-distances tend to be greater than S-distances, and for patterns with regularity, R-distances tend to be shorter than S-distances.

Exercise on Section 12

Exercise 12.1 Objects in a random pattern

The positions of objects in a large area may be assumed to be reasonably modelled by a two-dimensional Poisson process with density 0.2 per square metre.

(a) Find the expected distance from a randomly chosen point to the object nearest to it. Calculate the probability that the nearest object is more than 2 metres away.

(b) Find the mean and variance of the distance from a randomly selected object to the object nearest to it. Calculate the probability that the distance from a randomly selected object to the object nearest to it is less than 1 metre.

13 Detecting departures from randomness

Most patterns fall into one of three categories – random, regular or clustered – and it is natural to ask which category a particular pattern belongs to. In Section 12, you saw that counts in quadrats have different properties for patterns in the three categories, as do R-distances and S-distances. In this section, two tests of the null hypothesis that an observed spatial pattern is a random pattern are introduced. The test discussed in Subsection 13.1 uses counts in quadrats. The test described in Subsection 13.2 is based on R-distances and S-distances. Fixed-level testing is used to introduce the tests. Significance testing is discussed briefly in Subsection 13.3.

13.1 A test based on counts

The index of dispersion I for a spatial pattern was defined in Subsection 12.1 by

$$I = \frac{V(X)}{E(X)},$$

where X is the count of objects in the spatial pattern falling in any region of area A. You saw that, in general,

$$I > 1 \quad \text{for a clustered pattern,}$$
$$I = 1 \quad \text{for a random pattern,}$$
$$I < 1 \quad \text{for a regular pattern.}$$

This property of the index of dispersion can be used to develop a test of the null hypothesis that a spatial pattern is a random pattern.

Suppose that a region of a spatial pattern is divided into k non-overlapping quadrats, all of which have the same area A, and that the counts of objects observed in the quadrats are $x_1, x_2, \ldots, x_k$. Then the sample variance s^2 and the sample mean $\overline{x}$ of the observed counts provide estimates of $V(X)$ and $E(X)$, and hence the ratio $s^2/\overline{x}$ provides an estimate of the index of dispersion I. If the pattern is random, we should expect the value of the ratio to be reasonably close to 1. A value of $s^2/\overline{x}$ considerably greater than 1 would indicate clustering, and a value much less than 1 would indicate regularity.

This suggests that $S^2/\overline{X}$ might be a suitable test statistic, where

$$S^2 = \frac{1}{k-1}\sum_{i=1}^{k}\left(X_i - \overline{X}\right)^2, \quad \overline{X} = \frac{1}{k}\sum_{i=1}^{k} X_i,$$

and $X_1, \ldots, X_k$ are random variables representing the counts of objects in any k non-overlapping quadrats of area A. However, in practice, it is more convenient to use the test statistic $T = (k-1)S^2/\overline{X}$. Since $(k-1)S^2 = \sum_{i=1}^{k}(X_i - \overline{X})^2$ and $\overline{X} = (X_1 + \cdots + X_k)/k$, this can also be written as

$$T = \frac{k\sum_{i=1}^{k}\left(X_i - \overline{X}\right)^2}{M},$$

where $M = X_1 + \cdots + X_k$. This random variable is the test statistic for the χ^2 dispersion test, the details of which are summarised in the following box.

The χ^2 dispersion test

The χ^2 dispersion test is a two-sided test of the null hypothesis that a spatial pattern is a random pattern.

The test statistic is

$$T = \frac{k\sum_{i=1}^{k}\left(X_i - \overline{X}\right)^2}{M}, \tag{13.1}$$

where $X_1, \ldots, X_k$ are the counts of objects in k equal non-overlapping quadrats, and $M = X_1 + \cdots + X_k$ is the total number of objects in the quadrats.

The null distribution of T is approximately chi-squared with $k - 1$ degrees of freedom, provided that there are at least 20 objects in the pattern, with an average of at least four objects per quadrat, that is, provided that

$$M \geq 20 \quad \text{and} \quad M/k \geq 4. \tag{13.2}$$

Small values of T indicate regularity in the pattern; large values of T indicate clustering.

The use of this test is illustrated in Example 13.1 using a fixed-level approach.

Example 13.1 *Is the pattern random?*

In Example 10.3, the pattern of objects in a two-dimensional Poisson process was simulated over a square region. There were 35 objects in the simulated pattern, which is shown in Figure 10.5. The square region is divided into four quadrats in Figure 12.2; this figure is reproduced in Figure 13.1.

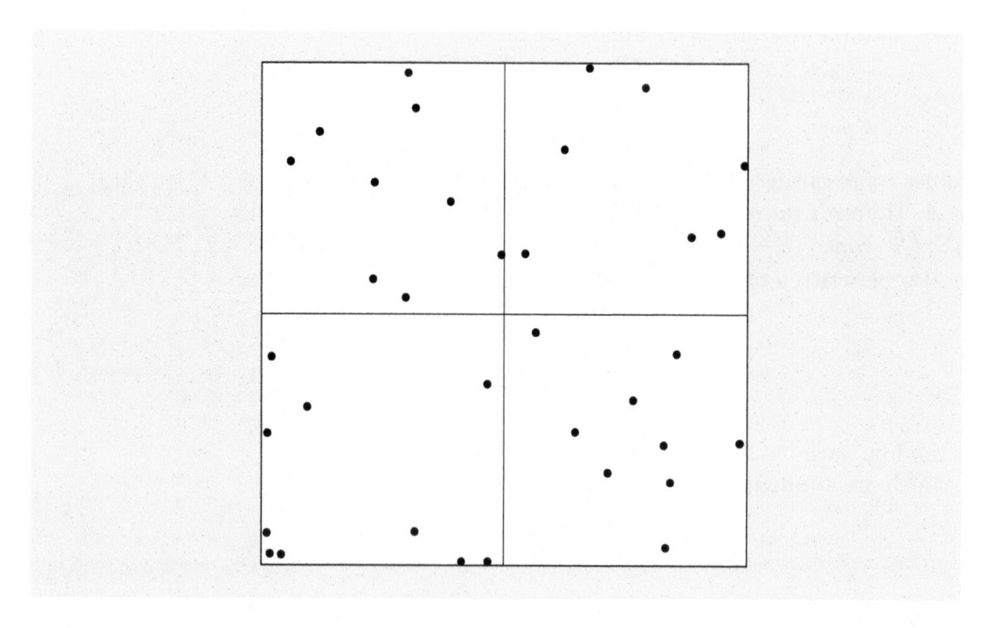

Figure 13.1 A simulated pattern

The χ^2 dispersion test will be used to test the null hypothesis that the pattern in Figure 13.1 is a random pattern. A fixed-level test will be carried out using a 5% significance level.

The first step is to check that the conditions of the test, given in (13.2), are satisfied. Since $M = 35$, which is greater than 20, the first condition is satisfied. Since $k = 4$, $M/k = 35/4 = 8.75$, so the second condition is also satisfied. Hence the χ^2 dispersion test can be used.

The next step is to find the null distribution of the test statistic T. Since $k = 4$, this is approximately $\chi^2(3)$.

Now find the rejection region for the test. This is given by

$$t \leq q_{0.025} \quad \text{and} \quad t \geq q_{0.975},$$

where $q_{0.025}$ is the 0.025-quantile and $q_{0.975}$ is the 0.975-quantile of $\chi^2(3)$. Table 3 in the *Handbook* contains quantiles for chi-squared distributions. Using this table, the required quantiles are 0.216 and 9.35, so the rejection region is given by

$$t \leq 0.216 \quad \text{and} \quad t \geq 9.35.$$

Next use the data to calculate the observed value t of T. From Figure 13.1, the observed counts are $x_1 = 9$, $x_2 = 7$, $x_3 = 10$ and $x_4 = 9$. Hence

For $k = 1, 2, \ldots,$

$$\sum_{i=1}^{k}(x_i - \overline{x})^2 = \sum_{i=1}^{k} x_i^2 - \left(\sum_{i=1}^{k} x_i\right)^2 \Big/ k.$$

$$\begin{aligned}\sum_{i=1}^{4}(x_i - \overline{x})^2 &= \sum_{i=1}^{4} x_i^2 - \left(\sum_{i=1}^{4} x_i\right)^2 \Big/ 4 \\ &= 311 - 35^2/4 \\ &= 4.75.\end{aligned}$$

Therefore the observed value of T is

$$t = \frac{k\sum_{i=1}^{k}(x_i - \overline{x})^2}{M} = \frac{4 \times 4.75}{35} \simeq 0.543.$$

This does not fall in the rejection region, so there is insufficient evidence to reject the null hypothesis that the pattern is a random pattern. (This is a relief, since the pattern was simulated using a spatially random model!) ♦

Activity 13.1 *White oak trees*

The positions of 211 white oak trees in a square-shaped region of Lansing Woods were shown in Figure 9.3. The pattern of the oak trees is reproduced in Figure 13.2, with the region divided into 25 equal-sized square quadrats.

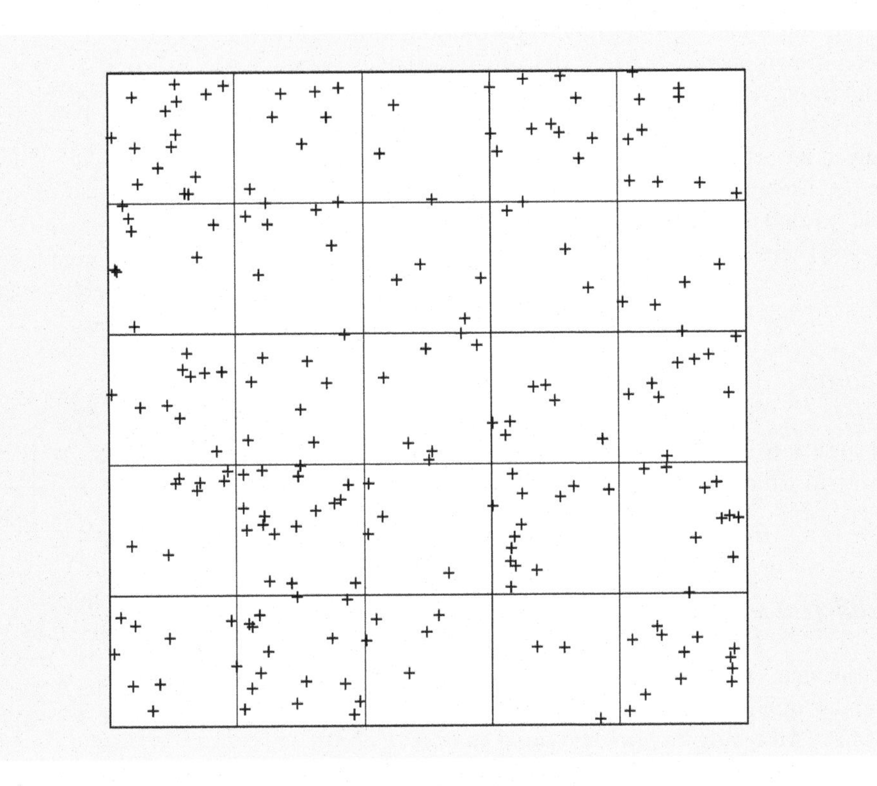

Figure 13.2 The positions of 211 white oak trees in Lansing Woods, Michigan

(a) Count the trees in each quadrat.

(b) Use the χ^2 dispersion test with a 5% significance level to investigate whether the pattern can reasonably be regarded as random.

If the test suggests that the white oaks are not randomly located, then say what sort of pattern you think they might follow, giving a reason for your answer.

The choice of quadrats

In Activity 13.1, counts were obtained by dividing the total area into 25 equal square-shaped quadrats. But do quadrats have to be square in shape? When the surveyed area is square, division into square quadrats is straightforward, but what if it is not square or even rectangular, but is irregular? And why was the area divided into 25 quadrats? How should the number of quadrats be chosen?

First consider the shape of quadrats. They do not have to be square. It does not matter what their shape is because the distribution of X, the number of objects in a random pattern falling in a region of area A, is the same whatever the shape of the region: if the density of objects is λ, then $X \sim \text{Poisson}(\lambda A)$. A situation where the quadrats are hexagonal is described in Example 13.2.

Example 13.2 *Quadrats*

Figure 13.3 shows the numbers of the large woodlouse *Philoscia muscorum* collected in 37 contiguous hexagonal quadrats of beech litter at Wythan Woods near Oxford on 30 October 1958. The quadrats are 1 ft across, so each has an area of 0.866 ft^2. The actual spatial pattern of objects is not given: the individual positions of the 53 woodlice were never recorded, only the counts in the quadrats.

Lloyd, M. (1967) 'Mean crowding', *Journal of Animal Ecology*, vol. 36, no.1, pp. 1–30.

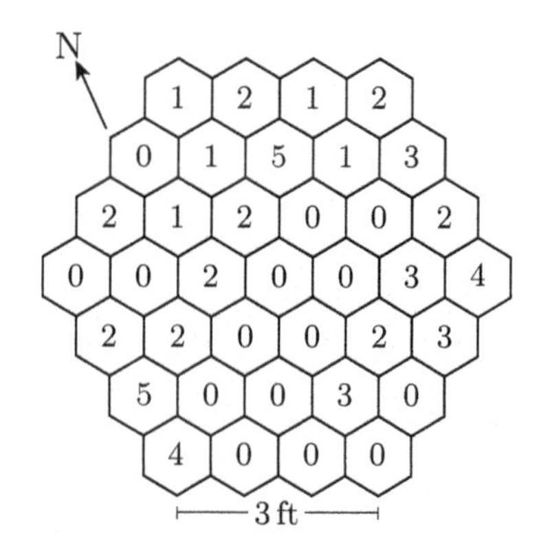

Figure 13.3 Numbers of the large woodlouse collected in hexagonal quadrats

There is another important feature of this data set. The hexagonal quadrats have a real existence as part of the zoological experiment: they are actual areas of beech litter marked out physically by the zoologist. However, in Figure 13.2, the pattern of white oaks was divided into 25 quadrats simply by drawing lines on a diagram of the pattern. The quadrats are a mere geometrical construction, and a different set of lines could have been drawn on the diagram that divided the pattern into a different array of quadrats. So there are cases where the quadrats are physical entities presented to the statistician as part of the data, and there are cases in which the statistician is given a pattern of object positions and can mark out quadrats, freely chosen for shape, size and position, on a map of the pattern. In the former situation, it may well be that only the counts of objects in the quadrats have been recorded, and not their individual positions. ♦

Activity 13.2 *Choosing quadrats*

Explain why it would not be appropriate to apply the χ^2 dispersion test to the counts in Figure 13.3. Suggest a way in which it might be possible to apply the test using these data.

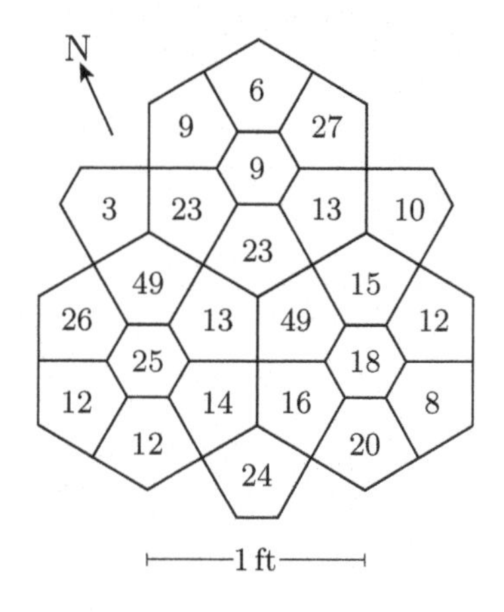

Figure 13.4 Numbers of the small woodlouse in equal-sized quadrats

Activity 13.3 *Quadrats of different shapes*

Figure 13.4 shows the numbers of the small woodlouse *Trichoniscus pusillus provisorius* in 24 very small contiguous quadrats of beech litter (data from the same source as those in Example 13.2). All quadrats have the same area (0.124 ft^2) but not the same shape. Explain whether the χ^2 dispersion test is appropriate for these data. If you think it is, then carry out the test using a 1% significance level.

For the white oak trees in Figure 13.2, the number of quadrats used and their pattern was open to choice. Since there are 211 trees, $M = 211$, and hence the first condition in (13.2) is satisfied. In order to meet the second condition, the average number of trees in a quadrat must be at least 4, that is, $M/k \geq 4$. Thus k can be chosen to be any convenient value up to about 55. The square area of survey divides naturally into square quadrats, so 25 is a suitable number, giving a substantial number of degrees of freedom (24) for the χ^2 dispersion test. To have used, say, 49 smaller quadrats would have involved substantial extra work in marking out the diagram and taking counts, without much advantage; while to have used a coarser division into, say, 16 or 9 square quadrats would have meant substantial loss of information. Alternatively, the area of survey could have been divided into 16 equal squares and then each square divided into two triangles by drawing in the SW/NE diagonal. This would have given 32 triangular quadrats. This is a perfectly good procedure, which is broadly equivalent to using 25 or 36 square quadrats.

If the surveyed area is not a square, then the pattern of quadrats can be chosen in many ways. It is important that the quadrats cover as much as possible of the area so that as little as possible of the information is lost.

Activity 13.4 Redwood seedlings

Look again at the pattern of 72 redwood seedlings in region I of Figure 9.6. Suppose that you were asked to test the pattern for randomness using the χ^2 dispersion test. How would you construct the quadrats?

Activity 13.5 London post offices

For the pattern of post offices in Figure 9.5, do you think it would be feasible to test for randomness using quadrat counts? If so, say briefly and without going into detail how you would set about doing it. What disadvantages do you think would be involved?

13.2 A test based on distances

In Section 12, the variate S was defined to be the distance from a randomly chosen *object* to the nearest object, and the variate R was defined as the distance from a randomly chosen *point* to the nearest object. You saw that:

◇ R and S have the same distribution for a random pattern;

◇ R-distances tend to exceed S-distances for a clustered pattern;

◇ S-distances tend to exceed R-distances for a pattern with regularity.

This suggests that samples of R-distances and S-distances could be used for detecting departures from randomness in a pattern. There are at least six different methods for doing this, and several further ones involving the distance from a randomly chosen point to the second nearest object. One of these methods, which dates from 1954 and is due to Hopkins, is discussed in this subsection. The test is summarised in the following box.

Hopkins, B. (1954) 'A new method of determining the type of distribution of plant individuals', *Annals of Botany*, vol. 18, no. 2, pp. 213–26.

Hopkins' test

Hopkins' test is a two-sided test of the null hypothesis that a spatial pattern is a random pattern.

The test statistic is

$$H = \sum_{i=1}^{n} R_i^2 \Bigg/ \sum_{i=1}^{n} S_i^2,$$

where the variates $R_1, \dots, R_n$ and $S_1, \dots, S_n$ are random samples of point-to-nearest-object distances and object-to-nearest-object distances, respectively.

The null distribution of H is $F(2n, 2n)$, the F distribution with degrees of freedom $\nu_1 = \nu_2 = 2n$.

Small values of H indicate regularity in the pattern; large values indicate clustering.

The family of F distributions is indexed by two parameters, known as degrees of freedom and denoted ν_1 and ν_2, and a typical member of the family is denoted $F(\nu_1, \nu_2)$. Table 4 in the *Handbook* contains quantiles for F distributions with degrees of freedom $\nu_1 = \nu_2 = 2n$. The rejection region for a fixed-level test can be found using appropriate quantiles from this table.

Since R-distances tend to be greater than S-distances for clustered patterns, an observed value of H considerably larger than 1 (in the upper tail of the null distribution of H) indicates clustering. An observed value of H considerably less than 1 (in the lower tail of the null distribution) indicates regularity, since R-distances tend to be less than S-distances for patterns with regularity. The use of Hopkins' test is illustrated in Example 13.3.

Example 13.3 London post offices

In Activity 13.5, you saw that using the χ^2 dispersion test to investigate whether the pattern of London post offices in Figure 9.5 is random is practicable, but the procedure is time-consuming. In a situation like this, Hopkins' test is more appropriate. In this example, Hopkins' test will be used with a 5% significance level to investigate the pattern of London post offices.

The map in Figure 9.5, which shows the positions of the 62 post offices in an area of London in the mid-1980s, is reproduced in Figure 13.5.

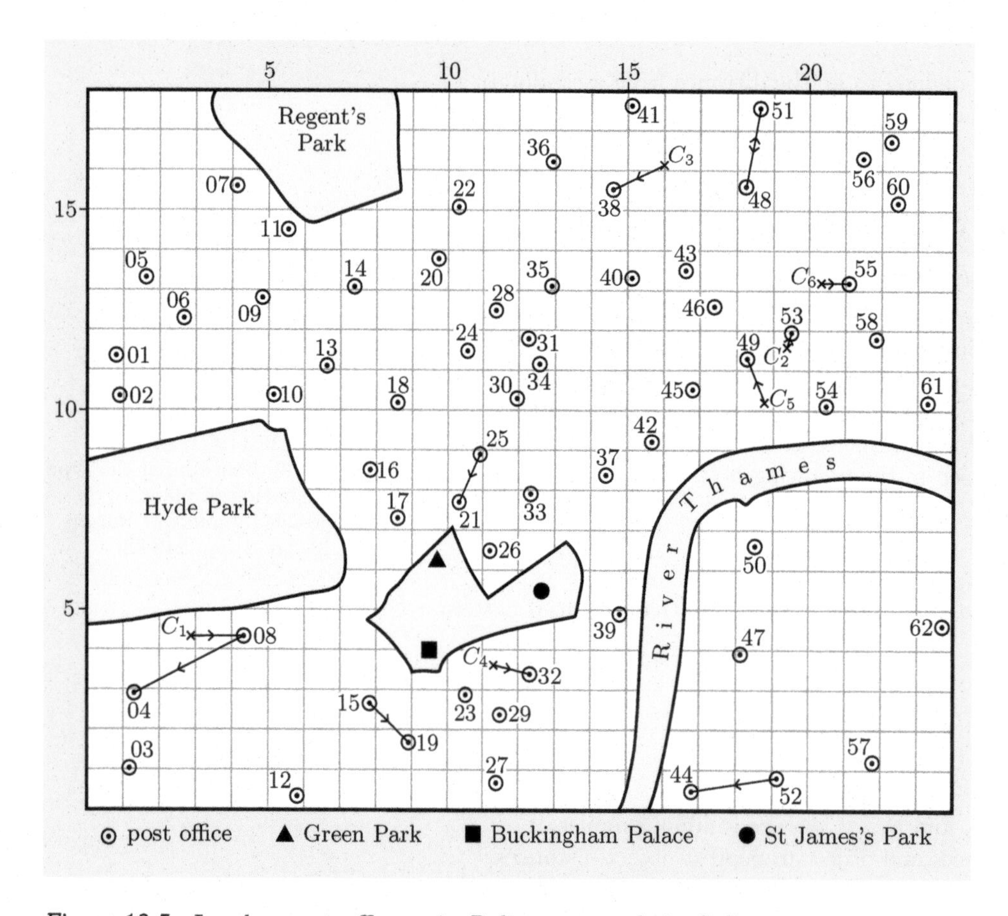

Figure 13.5 London post offices: six R-distances and six S-distances

Also shown in Figure 13.5 are the positions of six points selected at random (labelled $C_1, \ldots, C_6$) and six objects – post offices – selected at random from the 62 objects. (Note that if a point in the river or one of the parks were selected, it would be discarded because it is essential that all the points fall within the area of the survey.) For each point selected and each object selected, an arrow is drawn from the point or object to the object nearest to it.

Since the sample size n is 6, the null distribution of the test statistic H is $F(12, 12)$. For a 5% significance level, the 0.025-quantile and the 0.975-quantile of $F(12, 12)$ are required. From Table 4 in the *Handbook*, these are 0.305 and 3.277, so the rejection region for the test is

$$h \leq 0.305 \quad \text{and} \quad h \geq 3.277.$$

A scale is marked on Figure 13.5: the bottom left-hand corner of the map has coordinates $(0, 0)$, and the top right-hand corner is at $(24, 18)$. The six point-to-nearest-object distances and six object-to-nearest-object distances were calculated from the coordinates of the points and objects and their nearest objects. The six observed R-distances $r_1, \dots, r_6$, and six observed S-distances $s_1, \dots, s_6$, are given in Table 13.1.

Table 13.1 R-distances and S-distances

R-distances	1.4	0.4	1.5	0.9	1.2	0.8
S-distances	2.0	1.3	2.3	3.3	1.5	2.0

The observed value h of the test statistic H is

$$h = \sum_{i=1}^{6} r_i^2 \bigg/ \sum_{i=1}^{6} s_i^2 = 7.26/28.12 \simeq 0.258.$$

This is in the rejection region, so the null hypothesis that the pattern is a random pattern can be rejected at the 5% significance level.

Since the observed value $h = 0.258$ is considerably less than 1, there is some evidence of regularity in the pattern of post office locations. ♦

Activity 13.6 Redwood seedlings

In Example 9.5, it was suggested that the patterns of redwood seedlings in the two regions in Figure 9.6 might be different.

Random samples of five points and five objects were selected from region II, and the corresponding R-distances and S-distances were measured. The observed R-distances were 12, 9, 2, 3, 17, and the observed S-distances were 2, 6, 3, 1, 1. Carry out a test of the hypothesis that the seedlings in region II are distributed at random, using a 1% significance level.

13.3 Significance testing

In Subsections 13.1 and 13.2, the χ^2 dispersion test and Hopkins' test have been introduced using the fixed-level approach to hypothesis testing. For completeness, the application of these tests using the significance testing approach is discussed briefly in this subsection. If you have not met significance testing before, then you may wish to omit this subsection: familiarity with significance testing is assumed. In assignments and the examination, you may use either a fixed-level test or a significance test, whichever you prefer.

There are two main differences when performing a significance test instead of a fixed-level test. First, a p value is calculated instead of the rejection region for a fixed significance level. Second, the conclusion takes a slightly different form. The null distribution of the test statistic and the observed value of the test statistic are the same whichever approach is adopted.

To calculate the p value for either the χ^2 dispersion test or Hopkins' test requires the use of a statistical software package. However, the tables in the *Handbook* can be used to obtain an idea of the size of the p value. The use of Tables 3 and 4 is illustrated in Examples 13.4 and 13.5.

Example 13.4 χ^2 *dispersion test: the p value*

In Example 13.1, the χ^2 dispersion test was used to test the null hypothesis that the pattern in Figure 13.1 is a random pattern. The null distribution of the test statistic T is $\chi^2(3)$, and the observed value t of the test statistic is approximately 0.543.

From Table 3 in the *Handbook*, the 0.05-quantile of $\chi^2(3)$ is 0.352, and the 0.1-quantile is 0.584. Since $t = 0.543$ lies between these quantiles, it follows that

$$0.05 < P(T \leq 0.543) < 0.1.$$

The test is two-sided, so

$$0.1 < p < 0.2.$$ ♦

Example 13.5 *Hopkins' test: the p value*

In Example 13.3, Hopkins' test was used to test the null hypothesis that post offices are located randomly in an area of London. The null distribution of the test statistic H is $F(12, 12)$, and the observed value h of the test statistic is approximately 0.258.

From Table 4 in the *Handbook*, the 0.01-quantile of $F(12, 12)$ is 0.241, and the 0.025-quantile is 0.305. Since $h = 0.258$ lies between these quantiles, it follows that

$$0.01 < P(H \leq 0.258) < 0.025.$$

The test is two-sided, so

$$0.02 < p < 0.05.$$ ♦

The p value for a test is a measure of the strength of the evidence against the null hypothesis H_0. So the conclusion of a significance test involves interpreting the p value. A rough guide to the interpretation of p values is provided in Table 13.2.

Table 13.2 Interpretation of p values

p value	Rough interpretation
$p > 0.1$	Little evidence against H_0
$0.05 < p \leq 0.1$	Weak evidence against H_0
$0.01 < p \leq 0.05$	Moderate evidence against H_0
$p \leq 0.01$	Strong evidence against H_0

Example 13.6 *Test conclusions*

For the χ^2 dispersion test in Example 13.4, $0.1 < p < 0.2$. The conclusion of the test would be as follows. Since $p > 0.1$, there is little evidence against the null hypothesis that the pattern in Figure 13.1 is a random pattern.

For Hopkins' test in Example 13.5, $0.02 < p < 0.05$, so there is moderate evidence against the null hypothesis that the post offices are distributed randomly. Since the observed value h is considerably less than 1, there is evidence of regularity in the locations of the post offices. ♦

Activity 13.7 p values and conclusions

(a) In Activity 13.1, you found the null distribution and the observed value of the test statistic in a χ^2 dispersion test of the null hypothesis that the pattern of white oak trees shown in Figure 13.2 is a random pattern. What can you say about the p value for a significance test of this hypothesis? What would be the conclusion of the significance test?

(b) In Activity 13.6, you found the null distribution and the observed value of the test statistic when using Hopkins' test to test the null hypothesis that the redwood seedlings in region II of Figure 9.6 are randomly distributed in the region. What can you say about the p value for a significance test of this hypothesis? What would be the conclusion of the significance test?

13.4 Postscript

Part III of this book has contained a first look at the fascinating topic of spatial patterns and their properties. However, the broad classification regular/random/clustered does not cover all patterns. Consider, for example, a pattern of clusters of objects, where the cluster centres are, say, at the vertices of a square lattice! This pattern combines regularity of cluster centres with local clustering about these centres. What are its characteristics?

Spatial patterns present a wide field of problems, many of which have not been touched upon. For example, what sort of pattern results from the superposition of two known patterns? How can the relationship between two patterns be described in probabilistic terms? In the location diagram of ants' nests of two species shown in Figure 9.7, is there any evidence of interdependence between the positions of the two types of nest? For example, do *Cataglyphis* ants tend to nest near *Messor* ants, or perhaps, on the other hand, tend to avoid their nests?

For a simple sequential inhibition process, what is the average number of objects that can be placed in a given area before it is saturated, and what is the distribution of this number? How might a spatial pattern of trees be affected by the ages of the individual trees, and how might this be modelled?

Not all of these questions have yet been answered by research workers. Spatial processes are a popular and flourishing area of current research in probability and statistics.

Summary of Section 13

Two hypothesis tests for investigating whether a spatial pattern is a random pattern have been discussed in this section – the χ^2 dispersion test and Hopkins' test. The χ^2 dispersion test can be used when the data are in the form of counts in equal-sized quadrats, provided that the total count is at least 20 and the average number of objects in a quadrat is at least 4. Hopkins' test is appropriate when samples of point-to-nearest-object distances and object-to-nearest-object distances can be obtained. The tests have been described in the context of fixed-level testing. Significance testing has been discussed briefly.

Exercises on Section 13

Exercise 13.1 Testing for randomness using counts

The locations of plants in a rectangular area measuring 6 metres by 5 metres are recorded in an investigation into their reproductive behaviour.

The numbers of plants in square metre quadrats are as follows.

7	7	7	5	4	5
3	2	5	2	4	3
3	9	6	4	4	4
4	7	5	11	1	1
5	7	3	4	4	8

Use these data to investigate whether the plants can reasonably be supposed to be randomly located over the rectangle. Use a 5% significance level.

Exercise 13.2 Testing for randomness using distances

In a test of the pattern created by objects in two-dimensional space, eight R-distances and eight S-distances are recorded: $\sum r_i^2 = 2.7026$ and $\sum s_i^2 = 8.9320$.

(a) Carry out a test of the null hypothesis that the objects are randomly distributed. Use a 5% significance level.

If the test suggests that the objects are not randomly located, then say what form their pattern might take, giving a reason for your answer.

(b) What would the conclusion of the test be if a 1% significance level were used?

(c) Suppose that a significance test is performed instead of a fixed-level test. What can you say about the p value for the test? What is the conclusion of the test?

14 Exercises on Book 2

This section consists of exercises on *Book 2*; some of these exercises cover material from more than one section. The exercises in Subsection 14.1 provide practice in techniques and are of a routine nature. On the other hand, some of the exercises in Subsection 14.2 may involve further development of ideas and models from *Book 2*.

14.1 Routine exercises

Exercise 14.1 Failures of light bulbs

On average, a long-life light bulb fails in my house every ten months. When a bulb fails, it is replaced immediately. The occurrences of failures may be adequately modelled by a Poisson process.

(a) Suggest three random processes associated with this model. In each case, say whether the state space and the time domain are discrete or continuous.

(b) Calculate the probability that the interval between failures will exceed one year.

(c) Calculate the probability that exactly three light bulbs will fail in a two-year period.

Exercise 14.2 A Poisson process

Suppose that events occur according to a Poisson process with rate $\lambda = 2.4$ events per day.

(a) Calculate the mean number of events per week.

(b) Calculate the mean time between events.

(c) Calculate the probability that no event will occur during Monday next week.

(d) Calculate the probability that at least two events will occur during Tuesday next week.

Exercise 14.3 Arrivals at a petrol station

Cars arrive at a petrol station according to a Poisson process at the rate of one every five minutes. Commercial vehicles and motorcycles also arrive according to Poisson processes, with rates one every ten minutes and one every fifteen minutes, respectively. All vehicles arrive independently of each other.

(a) Calculate the probability that no vehicle will arrive for a period of five minutes.

(b) Calculate the probability that exactly four motorcycles will arrive in an hour.

(c) State the distribution of the times between the arrivals of successive vehicles.

(d) Calculate the probability that at least three cars or commercial vehicles will arrive in ten minutes.

(e) What is the probability that the next vehicle that arrives at the petrol station will be a car?

Exercise 14.4 A non-homogeneous Poisson process

The rate of occurrence of events in a non-homogeneous Poisson process is $\lambda(t) = 30t^2$.

(a) Calculate the probability that fewer than three events will occur by time $t = 0.5$.

(b) Calculate the probability that at most one event will occur in the interval $(0.5, 0.6]$.

(c) Given that five events occur in the interval $(0, 1]$, calculate the probability that they all occur after time $t = 0.5$.

Exercise 14.5 Another non-homogeneous Poisson process

The rate of occurrence of events in a non-homogeneous Poisson process is $\lambda(t) = 12te^{-2t}$.

(a) Sketch the graph of $\lambda(t)$ against t. When and at what value does the rate of occurrence of events peak?

(b) Calculate the probability that fewer than three events occur by time $t = 1$.

(c) Calculate the probability that one event occurs between $t = 1$ and $t = 2$.

(d) Find the total number of events expected after observation starts.

You will need to use integration by parts to find $\mu(t)$ in this exercise.

Exercise 14.6 Car occupants

Cars travel along a road according to a Poisson process with rate λ. It can be assumed that the number of people in a car is 1, 2, 3 or 4, with a discrete uniform distribution.

(a) Find the mean and variance of the number of occupants of a car.

(b) Find the mean and variance of the total number of occupants of cars that pass a point on the road in an interval of length t.

(c) Find the index of dispersion for this process. What does the value of the index of dispersion tell you about the process of car occupants passing the point on the road?

Exercise 14.7 A two-dimensional Poisson process

The positions of objects in a large area may be assumed to be reasonably modelled by a two-dimensional Poisson process with density $\lambda = 8 \times 10^{-4}$ per square metre. Part of the area is divided into cordoned rectangular regions, each 50 metres wide and 40 metres long.

(a) What is the probability distribution of the number of objects in a cordoned region?

(b) Calculate the probability that a cordoned region contains more than three objects.

(c) Use the number 0.9634, which is a random observation from the uniform distribution $U(0, 1)$, to simulate the number of objects in a cordoned region.

(d) Explain briefly, without carrying out the simulation, how you would simulate the positions of the objects in the region in part (c).

Exercise 14.8 Distances in a random pattern

The positions of objects in a large area may be assumed to be reasonably modelled by a two-dimensional Poisson process with density $\lambda = 8 \times 10^{-4}$ per square metre.

(a) Find the expected distance from a randomly chosen object to the object nearest to it. Calculate the probability that the nearest object is less than 10 metres away.

(b) Calculate the probability that the distance from a randomly chosen point to the object nearest to it is greater than 30 metres.

Exercise 14.9 Wild flowers in a wood

(a) The locations of wild flowers of a particular species in a wood are recorded, and the number of flowers, x, in each of 40 equal quadrats is counted: $\sum x_i = 180$, $\sum(x_i - \overline{x})^2 = 274$. Test whether the flowers can reasonably be supposed to be randomly located in the wood. Use a 5% significance level. If the test suggests that the flowers are not randomly located, then say how you think they are located, giving a reason for your answer.

(b) Suppose that a significance test is performed instead of a fixed-level test. What can you say about the p value for the test? What would be the conclusion of the test?

Exercise 14.10 Plants in a rectangular region

The locations of plants in a rectangular area measuring 6 metres by 5 metres are recorded in an investigation into their reproductive behaviour.

Twenty of the plants are selected at random, and the distance from each to its nearest neighbour is recorded. The 20 distances (in metres) are as follows.

0.20 0.31 0.37 0.23 0.16 0.35 0.34 0.36 0.23 0.35
0.27 0.32 0.07 0.24 0.33 0.45 0.30 0.16 0.57 0.33

At the same time, 20 points are selected at random in the region, and the distance from each to the nearest plant is recorded. These 20 distances (in metres) are as follows.

0.10 0.16 0.36 0.21 0.36 0.32 0.15 0.29 0.07 0.26
0.14 0.32 0.33 0.10 0.30 0.26 0.32 0.36 0.23 0.16

Use these data to investigate whether the plants can reasonably be supposed to be randomly located over the rectangle. Use a 5% significance level.

14.2 Further exercises

Exercise 14.11 Waiting times in a Poisson process

Suppose that events occur according to a Poisson process with rate $\lambda = 2.4$ events per day (that is, per 24 hours).

This is the Poisson process of Exercise 14.2.

(a) Find the probability density function of W_3, the waiting time until the third event after midnight tomorrow (where W_3 is measured in *hours*).

(b) Calculate the probability that the waiting time W_3 will exceed 30 hours.

Exercise 14.12 Waiting times

Suppose that each of n independent Poisson processes has rate λ.

(a) Find the distribution of U_1, the waiting time from the start of observation until one event (from any one of the processes) has occurred.

(b) Find the c.d.f. of U_2, the waiting time until at least one event has occurred in every process.

(c) Calculate the expected value of U_2 when $n = 2$.

Exercise 14.13 Insurance claims

Claims on household policies arrive at a small insurance office according to a Poisson process at the rate of three per day. The size of a claim in pounds has a gamma distribution $\Gamma(2, 0.016)$. Calculate the mean and variance of the total amount claimed over a 30-day period.

Exercise 14.14 Objects on a line

For a one-dimensional Poisson process of objects in space with density λ objects per unit length, find the distribution of the random variable S and state its mean. What is the distribution of R?

Exercise 14.15 The Rayleigh distribution

There are close connections between the Rayleigh distribution and two other standard distributions. In this exercise, you are invited to discover these connections for yourself.

(a) Suppose that R has a Rayleigh distribution with parameter λ. Find the c.d.f. of R^2, and hence identify the distribution of R^2.

(b) If $R_1, R_2, \ldots, R_n$ are independent random variables, each having a Rayleigh distribution with parameter λ, write down the distribution of $R_1^2 + R_2^2 + \cdots + R_n^2$.

Exercise 14.16 Lost in space

Objects are distributed in space at random according to a three-dimensional Poisson process with density λ. This implies that the probability that there is one object in any small region of volume δv is equal to $\lambda\,\delta v + o(\delta v)$.

(a) Obtain the c.d.f. of the distribution of the distance R from a point chosen at random to the object nearest to it.

The volume of a sphere of radius r is $\frac{4}{3}\pi r^3$.

(b) Find the median of R.

(c) Suppose that planets occur randomly in space with density 15 per cubic light-year, and that you are lost in space. Calculate the probability that there is no planet within a million million miles.

Take 1 year = 365.2425 days and c, the speed of light, to be 186 000 miles per second. A light-year is the distance that light travels in a year.

Summary of Book 2

Part I

Mathematically, a random process is defined to be a sequence (or collection) of random variables. It usually develops over time, though it can develop in space, and the time domain can be either continuous or discrete. The state space of a random process, which is the set of values that the random variables in the sequence can take, can be either continuous or discrete. The term 'random process' is used both to describe a developing physical situation and for a sequence of random variables associated with the situation. There may be several sequences of random variables (and thus several random processes) associated with a developing situation.

Part II

A point process is a random process that consists of events occurring in time. The notation $X(t)$ for the number of events in $(0, t]$, $X(t_1, t_2)$ for the number of events in $(t_1, t_2]$, T_n for the time between the $(n-1)$th and nth events, and W_n for the time from the start of observation until the nth event, is standard notation for point processes.

The Poisson process is a model for events occurring at random in continuous time at a rate that remains constant over time. This model assumes that events occur singly and independently. The number of events that occur in any fixed interval has a Poisson distribution, and the waiting time between successive events has an exponential distribution. The occurrences of events in a Poisson process can be simulated by simulating the times between successive events.

The Poisson process can be extended in several ways. The multivariate Poisson process is an extension in which each event is one of several types. For each type, the process of occurrences of events is itself a Poisson process. The non-homogeneous Poisson process is an extension of the Poisson process in which the rate at which events occur changes with time. In the compound Poisson process, multiple occurrences of events are allowed.

The index of dispersion for a point process is a measure that can be used to compare a point process with a Poisson process.

Part III

The two-dimensional Poisson process is a model for objects distributed randomly in two dimensions. The number or count of objects in any region of area A of a random pattern has a Poisson distribution. For a random pattern, the distributions of the point-to-nearest-object distance R and the object-to-nearest-object distance S are the same – a Rayleigh distribution.

There are two main ways in which a pattern may depart from randomness – by displaying either clustering or regularity. Models for patterns with clustering include the randomly-positioned clusters model (for clustering due to reproductive clumping) and the two-dimensional non-homogeneous Poisson process (for clustering due to heterogeneity of habitat). Models for patterns with regularity include lattice patterns with independent random displacements or with random deaths, and sequential inhibition processes.

The index of dispersion for a spatial pattern is a measure that can be used to compare a spatial pattern with a two-dimensional Poisson process. The χ^2 dispersion test, which is a test of the randomness of a spatial pattern, is based on the properties of the index of dispersion, and can be used with data in the form of quadrat counts, provided that certain conditions are satisfied. Hopkins' test, which is another test of the randomness of a spatial pattern, can be used with samples of R-distances and S-distances.

Learning outcomes

You have been working to develop the following skills.

Part I

- ◇ Identify sequences of random variables (random processes) associated with a physical process.
- ◇ Use the standard notation for random processes.
- ◇ Identify the time domain and the state space of a random process.
- ◇ Decide whether a process involving Bernoulli trials is a Bernoulli process.

Part II

- ◇ Define the random variables $X(t)$, $X(t_1, t_2)$, T_n and W_n for a point process, and use this notation when calculating probabilities associated with point processes.
- ◇ Calculate probabilities associated with the Poisson process, the multivariate Poisson process and the non-homogeneous Poisson process.
- ◇ Use relevant tables in the *Handbook* to simulate the occurrences of events in a Poisson process and in a non-homogeneous Poisson process.
- ◇ Calculate the mean and variance of the number of events that occur in an interval of given length in a compound Poisson process.
- ◇ Calculate and interpret the index of dispersion for a point process.

Part III

- ◇ Calculate probabilities associated with the two-dimensional Poisson process, and simulate the positions of objects in such a process.
- ◇ Derive the c.d.f. of the point-to-nearest-object distance R and the object-to-nearest-object distance S for a two-dimensional Poisson process.
- ◇ Describe the main features of the following models for spatial patterns: the two-dimensional Bernoulli process, lattice patterns with random displacements or random deaths, sequential inhibition processes and the randomly-positioned clusters model.
- ◇ Explain whether a particular model may or may not be appropriate for modelling the positions of objects in practical situations.
- ◇ Interpret the index of dispersion for a spatial pattern.
- ◇ Use the χ^2 dispersion test and Hopkins' test to test the hypothesis that a spatial pattern is a random pattern.

Solutions to Activities

Solution 1.1

The gambler's ruin The time domain of $\{X_n; n = 0, 1, \ldots\}$ is $\{0, 1, 2, \ldots\}$, which is discrete. The state space is $\{0, 1, \ldots, a\}$, which is also discrete.

Replacing light bulbs The time domain of $\{W_n; n = 1, 2, \ldots\}$ is $\{1, 2, 3, \ldots\}$, which is discrete. The replacement time of a light bulb is a continuous non-negative random variable, so the state space is $\{w : w \geq 0\}$, which is continuous.

Solution 1.2

(a) The time domain is $\{1, 2, \ldots\}$, which is discrete. For practical purposes, the amount of money (in £) spent by a customer can be treated as continuous, though it is actually an integral number of pence. In this case the state space is $\{a : a \geq 0\}$, and is continuous. (If A_n were modelled by a discrete random variable, then the state space would be $\{0, 0.01, 0.02, \ldots\}$.)

(b) The time domain is $\{t : 0 \leq t \leq 9\}$, which is continuous. The number of items sold by time t is a non-negative integer, so the state space is $\{0, 1, 2, \ldots\}$, which is discrete.

Solution 1.3

(a) The random variable Y_n represents the number of successes in n trials, so $Y_n \sim B(n, p)$.

(b) Since $Y_n = X_1 + \cdots + X_{n-1} + X_n = Y_{n-1} + X_n$, and it is known that $Y_{n-1} = y$, it follows that $Y_n = y + X_n$. Therefore Y_n will take the value y if $X_n = 0$ or $y + 1$ if $X_n = 1$, and

$$P(Y_n = y \mid Y_{n-1} = y) = P(X_n = 0) = 1 - p,$$
$$P(Y_n = y + 1 \mid Y_{n-1} = y) = P(X_n = 1) = p.$$

Solution 1.4

Another sequence of random variables associated with a Bernoulli process is $\{A_n; n = 1, 2, \ldots\}$, where A_n is the number of trials necessary to achieve the nth success. The random variable A_n has a negative binomial distribution with range $\{n, n + 1, \ldots\}$ and parameters n and p.

The random process has a discrete time domain and a discrete state space. The state space is $\{1, 2, \ldots\}$.

There are other possible sequences of random variables.

Solution 1.5

The changing weather from day to day may be well modelled by a Bernoulli process if (and only if!) it is reasonable to assume that the weather on any day is independent of the weather on preceding days, and if p, the probability of rain, does not vary from day to day.

Taken over a period of observation as long as a year, these assumptions would appear to fail: there will be 'wet spells' and 'dry spells'; and, in general, rain is more likely at some times of the year than at others. But over a shorter period, where perhaps seasonal variation may be discounted, the idea of a Bernoulli process might provide a useful model. (Actually, if a good model is required for representing the seasonal variation in weather, then it may be necessary to allow p to vary with n in some quite complicated way.)

Solution 2.1

The time domain of $\{Q(t); t \geq 0\}$ is continuous, but $\{L_n; n = 1, 2, \ldots\}$ and $\{W_n; n = 1, 2, \ldots\}$ have discrete time domains. The state space of $\{W_n; n = 1, 2, \ldots\}$ is $\{t : t \geq 0\}$, which is continuous. Both $\{Q(t); t \geq 0\}$ and $\{L_n; n = 1, 2, \ldots\}$ have state space $\{0, 1, 2, \ldots\}$, which is discrete.

Solution 2.2

Two random processes associated with the model for machine breakdowns are as follows.

$\{T_n; n = 1, 2, \ldots\}$, where T_n is the time at which the nth breakdown occurs. The time domain is $\{1, 2, \ldots\}$, which is discrete, and the state space is $\{t : t \geq 0\}$, which is continuous.

$\{Y(t); t \geq 0\}$, where $Y(t)$ is the number of breakdowns that have occurred by time t. The time domain is $\{t : t \geq 0\}$, which is continuous, and the state space is $\{0, 1, 2, \ldots\}$, which is discrete.

There are many other possibilities.

Solution 2.3

(a) If the customer has i different cards after $n - 1$ purchases, then the probability that he collects a new one at the nth purchase is $(20 - i)/20$. Hence X_n has a Bernoulli distribution with parameter $p = 1 - i/20$.

(b) This is not a Bernoulli process because the probability of 'success' (receiving a new card) changes during the process as new cards are acquired.

(c) Three possible sequences are given below; there are many others.

$\{Y_n; n = 1, 2, \ldots\}$, where Y_n denotes the number of different cards collected by the nth purchase. Both the time domain and the state space are discrete. The state space is $\{1, 2, \ldots, 20\}$.

$\{T_k; k = 1, 2, \ldots, 20\}$, where T_k is the number of purchases after the customer has $k - 1$ different cards until and including the purchase at which he receives the kth different card. Both the time domain and the state space are discrete. The state space is $\{1, 2, \ldots\}$.

$\{W_k; k = 1, 2, \ldots, 20\}$, where W_k is the total number of purchases required for the customer to obtain k different cards. Both the time domain and the state space are discrete. The state space is $\{1, 2, \ldots\}$.

Solution 2.4

The model is not a Bernoulli process because trials on successive days are not independent.

Solution 2.5

(a) Examples of suitable random processes are as follows.

$\{X(t); t \geq 0\}$, where $X(t)$ is the size of the colony at time t. $X(t)$ is discrete, t is continuous; so the state space is discrete and the time domain is continuous. The state space is $\{0, 1, 2, \ldots\}$.

$\{T_n; n = 1, 2, \ldots\}$, where T_n is the time between the $(n-1)$th and nth events, either divisions or deaths. The state space $\{t : t \geq 0\}$ is continuous, and the time domain is discrete.

$\{Y_n; n = 1, 2, \ldots\}$, where Y_n is the time between the $(n-1)$th and nth divisions. The state space $\{y : y \geq 0\}$ is continuous, and the time domain is discrete.

$\{Z_n; n = 1, 2, \ldots\}$, where Z_n is the time between the $(n-1)$th and nth deaths. The state space $\{z : z \geq 0\}$ is continuous, and the time domain is discrete.

Other possible processes include $\{W_n; n = 1, 2, \ldots\}$, where W_n is the time to the nth event, and $\{D_n; n = 1, 2, \ldots\}$, where D_n is the time to the nth death.

(b) Assuming that only one event (that is, one division or one death) occurs at any given time, your sketch should show steps of one unit up or down at random times. If the size $X(t)$ reaches 0, then it remains there, as there are then no bacteria to divide. A possible realisation is shown in Figure S.1.

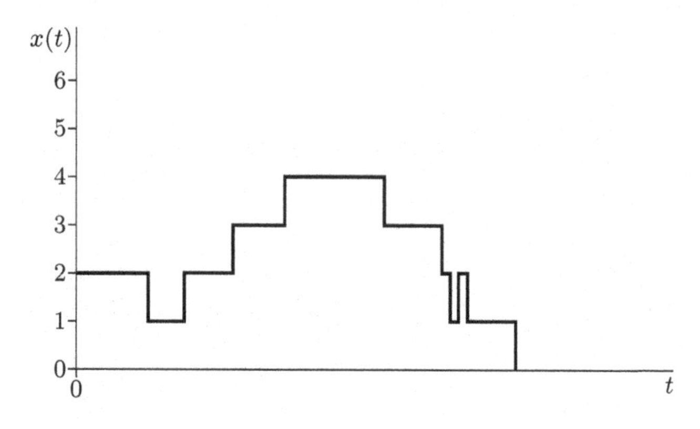

Figure S.1 A realisation of $\{X(t); t \geq 0\}$

Solution 3.1

(a) The rate of occurrence of nerve impulses is $\lambda = 458$ per second, and the length of the interval is $t = 0.01$ second. So $N(0.01)$, the number of impulses in 0.01 second, has a Poisson distribution with parameter

$$\lambda t = 458 \text{ per second} \times 0.01 \text{ second} = 4.58.$$

The probability required is

$$\begin{aligned} P(N(0.01) \leq 1) &= P(N(0.01) = 0) + P(N(0.01) = 1) \\ &= e^{-4.58} + \frac{e^{-4.58} \times 4.58}{1!} \\ &\simeq 0.0572. \end{aligned}$$

(b) The c.d.f. of T, the interval between successive impulses, is $F(t) = 1 - e^{-458t}$, so

$$P(T < \tfrac{1}{1000}) = F(\tfrac{1}{1000}) = 1 - e^{-0.458} \simeq 0.3675.$$

Solution 3.2

(a) The rate of the Poisson process is

$$\lambda = \tfrac{1}{14} \text{ per month.}$$

The number of major earthquakes that occur in a ten-year period, or 120 months, is $N(120)$, which has a Poisson distribution with parameter

$$\lambda t = \tfrac{1}{14} \text{ per month} \times 120 \text{ months} \simeq 8.571.$$

Hence the probability that there will be at least three major earthquakes in a ten-year period is

$$\begin{aligned} P(N(120) \geq 3) &= 1 - P(N(120) \leq 2) \\ &\simeq 1 - e^{-8.571}\left(1 + 8.571 + \frac{8.571^2}{2!}\right) \\ &\simeq 0.9912. \end{aligned}$$

(b) The waiting time (in months) between successive major earthquakes has an exponential distribution with parameter $\lambda = 1/14$. The probability that the waiting time exceeds two years, or 24 months, is given by

$$P(T > 24) = 1 - F(24) = e^{-24/14} \simeq 0.1801.$$

Solution 3.3

For the realisation in Figure 3.4, $X(1,3) = 3$, $X(4,5) = 0$, $X(0,2) = 3$, $X(1) = X(0,1) = 2$ and $X(3) = X(0,3) = 5$.

Solution 3.4

Since $W_n = T_1 + T_2 + \cdots + T_n$, it is the sum of n independent exponential random variables $T_1, T_2, \ldots, T_n$, each having parameter λ. Therefore W_n has a gamma distribution $\Gamma(n, \lambda)$.

Solution 3.5

Using the tenth row of the table of random numbers from $M(1)$, the simulation is as shown in Table S.1.

Table S.1 A simulation

n	e_n	$t_n = 652e_n$	$w_n = t_1 + \cdots + t_n$
1	1.5367	1001.9	1001.9
2	0.1395	91.0	1092.9
3	1.3503	880.4	1973.3
4	1.7518	1142.2	3115.5
5	1.6398	1069.1	4184.6

The first four failures occur at times $w_1 = 1001.9$, $w_2 = 1092.9$, $w_3 = 1973.3$, $w_4 = 3115.5$ (in seconds) – that is, after 1002 seconds, 1093 seconds, 1973 seconds and 3116 seconds (to the nearest second). The fifth failure occurs at time 4184.6, which is after the first hour of usage.

Solution 4.1

Setting $x = 2$ in (4.6) gives

$$\frac{dp_2(t)}{dt} = \lambda\, p_1(t) - \lambda\, p_2(t).$$

Substituting the known value of $p_1(t)$ in this differential equation gives

$$\frac{dp_2(t)}{dt} = \lambda^2 t e^{-\lambda t} - \lambda\, p_2(t),$$

or

$$\frac{dp_2(t)}{dt} + \lambda\, p_2(t) = \lambda^2 t e^{-\lambda t}.$$

Next, both sides of this equation are multiplied by the integrating factor, which is again $e^{\lambda t}$:

$$e^{\lambda t}\,\frac{dp_2(t)}{dt} + \lambda e^{\lambda t}\, p_2(t) = \lambda^2 t.$$

The left-hand side is the derivative of the product $e^{\lambda t} \times p_2(t)$, so the differential equation can be written as

$$\frac{d}{dt}\left(e^{\lambda t}\, p_2(t)\right) = \lambda^2 t.$$

Integrating both sides gives

$$e^{\lambda t}\, p_2(t) = \int \lambda^2 t\, dt = \tfrac{1}{2}\lambda^2 t^2 + c.$$

At time $t = 0$, no event has occurred, so $p_2(0) = P(X(0) = 2) = 0$, and hence $c = 0$. Thus

$$e^{\lambda t}\, p_2(t) = \tfrac{1}{2}\lambda^2 t^2,$$

so

$$p_2(t) = \tfrac{1}{2}\lambda^2 t^2 e^{-\lambda t},$$

which can be rewritten as

$$p_2(t) = \frac{e^{-\lambda t}(\lambda t)^2}{2}.$$

Solution 5.1

The probabilities that an arriving customer is of types A, B and C are $p_{\rm A} = 0.6$, $p_{\rm B} = 0.3$ and $p_{\rm C} = 0.1$, respectively, and $\lambda = 10$ per minute, so

$$\lambda_{\rm A} = \lambda p_{\rm A} = 6 \text{ per minute},$$
$$\lambda_{\rm B} = \lambda p_{\rm B} = 3 \text{ per minute},$$
$$\lambda_{\rm C} = \lambda p_{\rm C} = 1 \text{ per minute}.$$

(a) If $N(t)$ denotes the number of customers who arrive in an interval of length t minutes, then the number of customers who arrive in 30 seconds, or 0.5 minute, is $N(0.5)$, which has a Poisson distribution with parameter

$$\lambda t = (10 \text{ per minute}) \times (0.5 \text{ minute}) = 5.$$

Therefore

$$\begin{aligned} P(N(0.5) > 5) &= 1 - P(N(0.5) \leq 5) \\ &= 1 - e^{-5}\left(1 + 5 + \frac{5^2}{2!} + \frac{5^3}{3!} + \frac{5^4}{4!} + \frac{5^5}{5!}\right) \\ &\simeq 0.3840. \end{aligned}$$

(b) Let $A(t)$ represent the number of customers of type A who arrive in an interval of length t minutes. Then the number of customers of type A who arrive in one minute is $A(1)$, which has a Poisson distribution with parameter

$$\lambda_{\rm A} t = (6 \text{ per minute}) \times (1 \text{ minute}) = 6.$$

Therefore

$$P(A(1) = 6) = \frac{e^{-6}6^6}{6!} \simeq 0.1606.$$

(c) Customers of different types arrive independently, so the probability required is given by the product

$$\begin{aligned} &\frac{e^{-6}6^6}{6!} \times \frac{e^{-3}3^3}{3!} \times \left(1 - e^{-1}\right) \\ &\simeq 0.1606 \times 0.2240 \times 0.6321 \\ &\simeq 0.0227. \end{aligned}$$

Solution 5.2

If calls from students are type 1, from family are type 2, and from friends are type 3, then

$$\lambda_1 = 1 \text{ per 90 minutes} = \tfrac{2}{3} \text{ per hour},$$
$$\lambda_2 = 1 \text{ per 3 hours} = \tfrac{1}{3} \text{ per hour},$$
$$\lambda_3 = 1 \text{ per hour}.$$

(a) The rate at which telephone calls arrive is given by

$$\lambda = \lambda_1 + \lambda_2 + \lambda_3 = 2 \text{ per hour}.$$

If $N(t)$ is the number of calls that arrive in t hours, then the number of calls between 7 pm and 9 pm is $N(2)$, which has a Poisson distribution with parameter $\lambda t = 4$. The probability that there will be no calls is given by

$$P(N(2) = 0) = e^{-4} \simeq 0.0183.$$

(b) The proportion of calls that are from students is

$$p_1 = \frac{\lambda_1}{\lambda_1 + \lambda_2 + \lambda_3} = \tfrac{2}{3}/2 = \tfrac{1}{3}.$$

So the probability that the first call after 9 pm is from a student is $\frac{1}{3}$.

(c) The probability that a call received is from a family member is

$$p_2 = \frac{\lambda_2}{\lambda_1+\lambda_2+\lambda_3} = \tfrac{1}{3}/2 = \tfrac{1}{6}.$$

Since calls of different types arrive independently, and the probability that each call is from a family member is $\frac{1}{6}$, N, the number of calls out of 4 that are from family members, has a binomial distribution: $N \sim B(4, \frac{1}{6})$.

The probability required is

$$P(N=2) = \binom{4}{2}\left(\tfrac{1}{6}\right)^2\left(\tfrac{5}{6}\right)^2 = \tfrac{25}{216} \simeq 0.1157.$$

Solution 6.1

A possible sketch of the arrival rate $\lambda(t)$ is shown in Figure S.2.

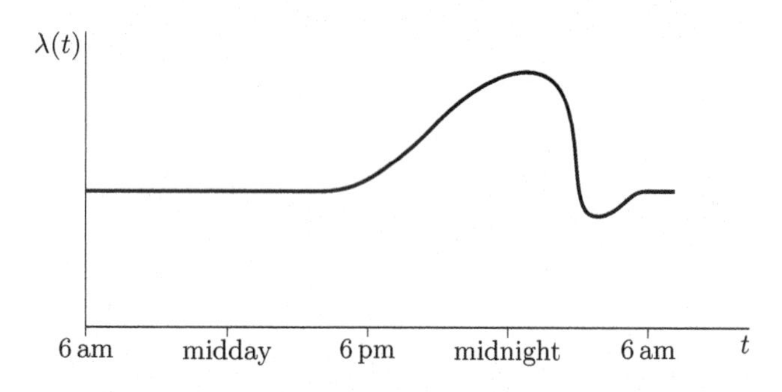

Figure S.2 Arrival rate at an accident and emergency unit over a 24-hour period

Solution 6.2

(a) The expected number of accidents in the first t days is given by

$$\begin{aligned}\mu(t) = \int_0^t \lambda(u)\,du &= \int_0^t \frac{24}{2+u}\,du \\ &= \big[24\log(2+u)\big]_0^t \\ &= 24\log(2+t) - 24\log 2 \\ &= 24\log\frac{2+t}{2} \\ &= 24\log\left(1+\frac{t}{2}\right).\end{aligned}$$

(b) The expected number of accidents during the first week ($t = 7$ days) is

$$\mu(7) = 24\log 4.5 \simeq 36.1.$$

Remember that in M343 'log' refers to logarithms to base e and that on most calculators you need to use the key labelled 'ln'.

(c) The expected number of accidents during the third week ($t_1 = 14$ days, $t_2 = 21$ days) is

$$\begin{aligned}\mu(14,21) &= \mu(21) - \mu(14) \\ &= 24\log 11.5 - 24\log 8 \\ &\simeq 8.71.\end{aligned}$$

The number of accidents has a Poisson distribution with parameter 8.71, so the probability required is

$$P(X(14,21) = 8) = \frac{e^{-8.71}8.71^8}{8!} \simeq 0.135.$$

(d) The expected number of accidents during the fourth week is

$$\begin{aligned}\mu(21,28) &= \mu(28) - \mu(21) \\ &= 24\log 15 - 24\log 11.5 \\ &\simeq 6.38.\end{aligned}$$

Therefore the number of accidents in the fourth week has a Poisson distribution with parameter 6.38.

The probability that the fourth week is free of accidents is

$$P(X(21,28) = 0) = e^{-6.38} \simeq 0.0017.$$

Solution 6.3

(a) The expected number of events by time t is given by

$$\mu(t) = \int_0^t \lambda(u)\,du = \int_0^t 2u\,du = \big[u^2\big]_0^t = t^2.$$

(b) Using (6.5), the c.d.f. of T_1, the time until the first event, is

$$F_{T_1}(t) = 1 - e^{-\mu(t)} = 1 - e^{-t^2}.$$

Therefore

$$P(T_1 > t) = 1 - F_{T_1}(t) = e^{-t^2}, \quad t \geq 0.$$

(c) The easiest way to find the expected value of T_1 is to use the alternative formula for the mean:

$$\begin{aligned}E(T_1) &= \int_0^\infty (1 - F_{T_1}(t))\,dt \\ &= \int_0^\infty P(T_1 > t)\,dt \\ &= \int_0^\infty e^{-t^2}\,dt.\end{aligned}$$

Setting $\alpha = 1$ in the standard result

$$\int_{-\infty}^{\infty} e^{-\alpha x^2}\,dx = \sqrt{\frac{\pi}{\alpha}}$$

gives

$$\int_{-\infty}^{\infty} e^{-x^2}\,dx = \sqrt{\pi}.$$

Since e^{-x^2} is symmetric about $x = 0$,

$$\int_0^\infty e^{-x^2}\,dx = \tfrac{1}{2}\sqrt{\pi},$$

and hence

$$E(T_1) = \tfrac{1}{2}\sqrt{\pi}.$$

(d) Using (6.6), the c.d.f. of T is

$$\begin{aligned}F_T(t) &= 1 - e^{-\mu(v,t)} \\ &= 1 - e^{-(\mu(t)-\mu(v))} \\ &= 1 - e^{-(t^2-v^2)}.\end{aligned}$$

Therefore

$$P(T > t) = 1 - F_T(t) = e^{-(t^2-v^2)}.$$

Solution 6.4

From the solution to part (a) of Activity 6.3,

$$\mu(t) = t^2, \quad t > 0.$$

Using (6.7), w_1 is the solution of

$$w_1^2 = -\log(1 - u_1) = -\log(1 - 0.622) \simeq 0.972\,86,$$

so

$$w_1 \simeq 0.986.$$

Using (6.8) gives

$$w_2^2 = w_1^2 - \log(1 - u_2),$$

which leads to

$$w_2 \simeq 1.116.$$

Using (6.8) again gives

$$w_3^2 = w_2^2 - \log(1 - u_3),$$

which leads to

$$w_3 \simeq 1.655.$$

Solution 6.5

From the solution to part (a) of Activity 6.3, $\mu(t) = t^2$, so (6.8) reduces to

$$w_{j+1}^2 = w_j^2 - \log(1 - u),$$

and hence

$$w_{j+1} = \sqrt{w_j^2 - \log(1 - u)}.$$

Setting $w_0 = 0$ in this recurrence relation gives

$$\begin{aligned}
w_1 &= \sqrt{-\log(1 - 0.927)} \simeq \sqrt{2.6173} \simeq 1.618,\\
w_2 &= \sqrt{2.6173 - \log(1 - 0.098)} \simeq \sqrt{2.7204} \simeq 1.649,\\
w_3 &= \sqrt{2.7204 - \log(1 - 0.397)} \simeq \sqrt{3.2263} \simeq 1.796,\\
w_4 &= \sqrt{3.2263 - \log(1 - 0.604)} \simeq \sqrt{4.1526} \simeq 2.038.
\end{aligned}$$

(Full calculator accuracy has been retained throughout these calculations.)

Solution 7.1

(a) The mean (expected value) of Y is

$$\begin{aligned}
\mu = E(Y) &= \sum y\, P(Y = y)\\
&= 0 \times 0.2 + 1 \times 0.3 + 2 \times 0.4 + 3 \times 0.1\\
&= 0 + 0.3 + 0.8 + 0.3\\
&= 1.4.
\end{aligned}$$

The expected value of Y^2 is

$$\begin{aligned}
E(Y^2) &= 0^2 \times 0.2 + 1^2 \times 0.3 + 2^2 \times 0.4 + 3^2 \times 0.1\\
&= 0 + 0.3 + 1.6 + 0.9\\
&= 2.8.
\end{aligned}$$

So the variance of Y is

$$\begin{aligned}
\sigma^2 = V(Y) &= E(Y^2) - (E(Y))^2\\
&= 2.8 - 1.4^2\\
&= 0.84.
\end{aligned}$$

(b) The departure rate of shoppers is 1 per 5 minutes or 12 per hour, so $\lambda = 12$ per hour. The interval of observation is $t = 3$ hours.

Therefore, using (7.5) and (7.6), the mean and variance of the total number of items purchased are given by

$$E[S(3)] = 1.4 \times 12 \times 3 = 50.4,$$
$$V[S(3)] = 12 \times 3 \times \left(0.84 + 1.4^2\right) = 100.8.$$

Solution 7.2

If $Y_i \sim G_0(\alpha)$, then

$$\mu = E(Y_i) = \frac{\alpha}{1-\alpha},$$
$$\sigma^2 = V(Y_i) = \frac{\alpha}{(1-\alpha)^2}.$$

Therefore

$$E[S(t)] = \mu\lambda t = \frac{\alpha\lambda t}{1-\alpha},$$

$$\begin{aligned}
V[S(t)] = \lambda t(\sigma^2 + \mu^2) &= \lambda t\left[\frac{\alpha}{(1-\alpha)^2} + \frac{\alpha^2}{(1-\alpha)^2}\right]\\
&= \frac{\alpha(1+\alpha)\lambda t}{(1-\alpha)^2}.
\end{aligned}$$

Solution 7.3

(a) Let the random variable Y_i take the value 1 if the event is recorded, and 0 if it is not. That is,

$$P(Y_i = 1) = p, \quad P(Y_i = 0) = 1 - p,$$

and $Y_i \sim B(1, p)$. Therefore

$$\mu = E(Y_i) = p, \quad \sigma^2 = V(Y_i) = p(1-p).$$

Hence

$$E[S(t)] = \mu\lambda t = p\lambda t,$$
$$V[S(t)] = \lambda t(\sigma^2 + \mu^2) = \lambda t(p(1-p) + p^2) = p\lambda t.$$

(b) The mean and variance of $S(t)$ are equal. This equality suggests that a Poisson distribution is a possibility. In fact, $S(t) \sim \text{Poisson}(\lambda t)$.

This result follows from a consideration of Postulate I for the Poisson process. If the probability that exactly one event *occurs* in the time interval $[t, t + \delta t]$ is equal to $\lambda\,\delta t + o(\delta t)$, and the probability that it is detected is p, then the probability that an event is *detected* in the time interval $[t, t + \delta t]$ is $p\lambda\,\delta t + o(\delta t)$. Hence events are detected according to a Poisson process with rate $p\lambda$, and therefore the number of events detected in an interval of length t has a Poisson distribution with parameter $p\lambda t$.

Solution 8.1

For a non-homogeneous Poisson process, $X(t) \sim \text{Poisson}(\mu(t))$, so

$$E[X(t)] = V[X(t)] = \mu(t).$$

Therefore

$$I(t) = \frac{V[X(t)]}{E[X(t)]} = 1.$$

That is, the index of dispersion for a non-homogeneous Poisson process is the same as that for a Poisson process.

Solution 8.2

(a) Using (8.1),

$$I(t) = \frac{\sigma^2}{\mu} + \mu = \frac{0.84}{1.4} + 1.4 = 2.$$

(b) The index of dispersion exceeds 1, so the pattern of purchases is more variable than it would be if purchases occurred according to a Poisson process.

Solution 8.3

When $Y \sim G_0(\alpha)$,

$$\mu = E(Y) = \frac{\alpha}{1-\alpha}, \quad \sigma^2 = V(Y) = \frac{\alpha}{(1-\alpha)^2}.$$

Therefore, using (8.1),

$$\begin{aligned} I(t) &= \frac{\sigma^2}{\mu} + \mu \\ &= \frac{\alpha/(1-\alpha)^2}{\alpha/(1-\alpha)} + \frac{\alpha}{1-\alpha} \\ &= \frac{1}{1-\alpha} + \frac{\alpha}{1-\alpha} \\ &= \frac{1+\alpha}{1-\alpha}. \end{aligned}$$

Solution 8.4

When $Y \sim \text{Poisson}(\mu)$, $\sigma^2 = V(Y) = \mu$, so

$$I(t) = \frac{\sigma^2}{\mu} + \mu = \frac{\mu}{\mu} + \mu = 1 + \mu.$$

Solution 10.1

(a) The number of primroses in a square of area 1 square metre, N, has a Poisson distribution with parameter 1.2, so

$$P(N = 3) = \frac{e^{-1.2}1.2^3}{3!} \simeq 0.0867.$$

(b) The shape of the region is irrelevant, so this probability is also 0.0867.

(c) The probability required is

$$P(N = 0) = e^{-1.2} \simeq 0.3012.$$

(d) The number of primroses in an area of 2 square metres, Y, has a Poisson distribution with parameter

$$\lambda A = 1.2 \times 2 = 2.4.$$

Therefore

$$\begin{aligned} P(Y \geq 5) &= 1 - P(Y \leq 4) \\ &= 1 - e^{-2.4}\left(1 + 2.4 + \frac{2.4^2}{2!} + \frac{2.4^3}{3!} + \frac{2.4^4}{4!}\right) \\ &\simeq 1 - 0.9041 \\ &= 0.0959. \end{aligned}$$

Solution 10.2

The number of objects on the line is an observed value n of $N \sim \text{Poisson}(4)$. Values of the c.d.f. of N are given in Table 10.1. Using the first four digits from Row 30 of Table 5 in the *Handbook* gives $u = 0.2386$. Since

$$F(2) = 0.2381 < 0.2386 < 0.4335 = F(3),$$

the simulated number of objects is $n = 3$. Hence the positions P_1, P_2, P_3 of three objects need to be simulated.

Continuing along Row 30, using groups of three digits gives $u_1 = 0.189$, $u_2 = 0.242$, $u_3 = 0.891$. The lengths AP_1, AP_2 and AP_3 are observations from $U(0, 40)$, so

$$\begin{aligned} AP_1 &= 0.189 \times 40 = 7.56, \\ AP_2 &= 0.242 \times 40 = 9.68, \\ AP_3 &= 0.891 \times 40 = 35.64. \end{aligned}$$

The simulated positions of the objects are illustrated in Figure S.3.

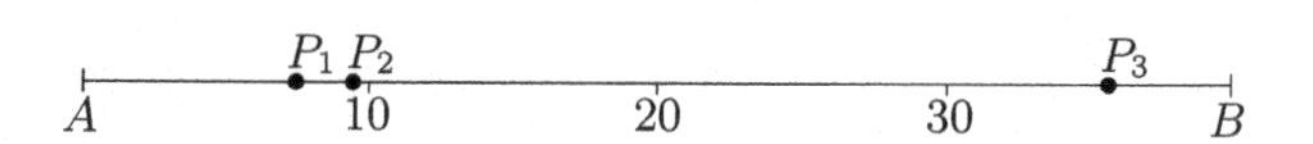

Figure S.3 A realisation of a Poisson process

Solution 10.3

The number of plants, N, in a region of area 2.5×1.6 square metres has a Poisson distribution with parameter

$$\lambda A = 1.2 \times 2.5 \times 1.6 = 4.8.$$

Values of the c.d.f. of N are given in Table S.2.

Table S.2 Values of the c.d.f. of N

n	0	1	2	3	...
$F(n)$	0.0082	0.0477	0.1425	0.2942	...

Given $u = 0.1471$, since

$$F(2) = 0.1425 < 0.1471 < 0.2942 = F(3),$$

the simulated number of plants is 3.

For each plant, two random values from $U(0, 1)$ are required. The first value is multiplied by 2.5, and the second by 1.6, to give the coordinates of the plant's position. Taking groups of three digits from Row 16 and rounding the coordinates to two decimal places leads to the results given in Table S.3.

Table S.3 Positions of three plants

Plant	u_1	u_2	$(2.5u_1, 1.6u_2)$
P_1	0.206	0.402	$(0.52, 0.64)$
P_2	0.949	0.371	$(2.37, 0.59)$
P_3	0.687	0.866	$(1.72, 1.39)$

The positions of the plants are shown in Figure S.4.

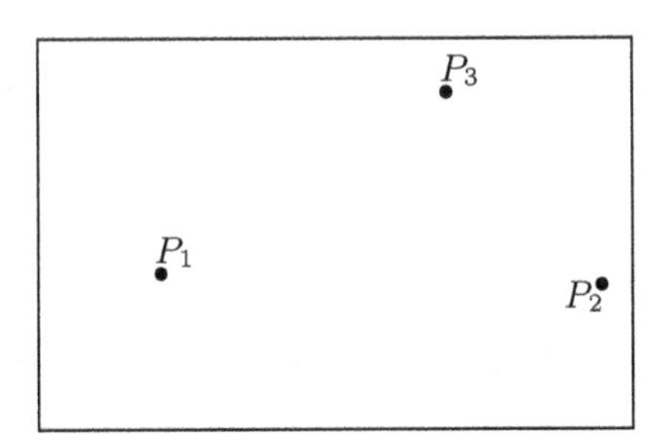

Figure S.4 Positions of plants in a simulation

Solution 10.4

First, draw a rectangle that includes the irregular area completely. The sides may be in any convenient directions. Then, using the method already described, simulate a two-dimensional Poisson process with the given density over the entire rectangle. If a simulated point falls within the irregular area, it forms part of the simulated pattern; if it is outside the area, then it is ignored.

Solution 11.1

Since the probability that a tree dies is p, the probability that a tree survives is $1 - p$. The deaths occur independently, so the pattern is a two-dimensional Bernoulli process with parameter $1 - p$.

Solution 11.2

The model of random deaths assumes that death occurs independently from tree to tree. In a real-life situation, a tree might well be more likely to die if adjacent to a diseased (and subsequently dead) tree than if surrounded by healthy trees; that is, disease could occur by contagion. So the assumption of independence could well be unrealistic.

Solution 11.3

There is no single correct answer to this activity. One possible answer is as follows.

(a) People tend to live in family groups, so the positions of people tend to be clustered. Assuming that family groups are randomly located, a randomly-positioned clusters model might be more suitable than a two-dimensional Poisson process.

(b) Since there is a limit to how close two farmhouses are likely to be, a sequential inhibition process might be more appropriate. (Positions are more regularly distributed than in a two-dimensional Poisson process.)

Solution 12.1

The number of lattice points in a rectangular quadrat of size $a \times b$ is ab. So X, the number of objects in a quadrat, has the binomial distribution $B(ab, p)$. Therefore $E(X) = abp$ and $V(X) = abp(1 - p)$, and hence $I = 1 - p$.

Solution 12.2

(a) The object nearest to P_{18} is P_2. The value of S for P_{18} is the same as for P_2, that is, 1.41.

(b) The object nearest to P_7 is P_{26}, but the object nearest to P_{26} is P_{19}, not P_7. Therefore if P_j is the object nearest to P_i, then P_i is not necessarily the object nearest to P_j.

Solution 12.3

The median m satisfies the equation $F(m) = 0.5$, that is,

$$1 - e^{-\pi\lambda m^2} = 0.5.$$

Therefore

$$m^2 = -\frac{\log 0.5}{\pi\lambda} \simeq \frac{0.693}{\pi\lambda},$$

and hence

$$m \simeq \frac{0.47}{\sqrt{\lambda}}.$$

The mean is $0.5/\sqrt{\lambda}$, so the median is a little less than the mean.

Solution 12.4

The variance of the Rayleigh distribution can be found using

$$V(X) = E(X^2) - [E(X)]^2.$$

Now

$$\begin{aligned}E(X^2) &= \int_0^\infty x^2 f(x)\,dx \\ &= \int_0^\infty x^2 \times 2\pi\lambda x e^{-\pi\lambda x^2}\,dx \\ &= \int_0^\infty 2\pi\lambda x^3 e^{-\pi\lambda x^2}\,dx.\end{aligned}$$

Using integration by parts gives

$$\begin{aligned}E(X^2) &= \left[-x^2 e^{-\pi\lambda x^2}\right]_0^\infty + \int_0^\infty 2x e^{-\pi\lambda x^2}\,dx \\ &= 0 + \left[-\frac{e^{-\pi\lambda x^2}}{\pi\lambda}\right]_0^\infty \\ &= \frac{1}{\pi\lambda}.\end{aligned}$$

From (12.4), $E(X) = 0.5/\sqrt{\lambda}$, so

$$V(X) = \frac{1}{\pi\lambda} - \left(\frac{0.5}{\sqrt{\lambda}}\right)^2 = \frac{1}{\pi\lambda} - \frac{1}{4\lambda} = \frac{4-\pi}{4\pi\lambda}.$$

The standard deviation is $\sqrt{V(X)} \simeq 0.26/\sqrt{\lambda}$.

Solution 12.5

The point-to-nearest-object distance R and the object-to-nearest-object distance S (measured in km) both have a Rayleigh distribution with parameter $\lambda = 60$ per km^2 and c.d.f.

$$F(x) = 1 - e^{-\pi\lambda x^2}, \quad x > 0.$$

(a) Using (12.4), the mean object-to-nearest-object distance in kilometres is

$$E(S) = \frac{0.5}{\sqrt{60}} \simeq 0.0645.$$

That is, $E(S) \simeq 64.5\,\text{m}$.

Since $100\,\text{m} = 0.1\,\text{km}$, the probability required is

$$P(S > 0.1) = e^{-\pi\times 60\times 0.1^2} \simeq 0.152.$$

(b) The mean point-to-nearest-object distance, $E(R)$, is also given by (12.4), so $E(R) \simeq 64.5\,\text{m}$.

Since $50\,\text{m} = 0.05\,\text{km}$, the probability required is

$$P(R < 0.05) = 1 - e^{-\pi\times 60\times 0.05^2} \simeq 0.376.$$

Solution 13.1

(a) The 25 quadrat counts are as follows. (You may have made a different decision about allocating borderline cases to quadrats.)

15	8	5	9	10
8	6	4	4	4
10	8	7	7	10
8	17	4	13	9
9	15	5	3	13

(b) There are 25 quadrats, so $k = 25$, and the total count M is 211, hence $M > 20$ and $M/k = 8.44 > 4$. So the conditions for applying the χ^2 dispersion test are satisfied.

Since $k = 25$, the null distribution of T is approximately $\chi^2(24)$. From Table 3 in the *Handbook*, the 0.025-quantile of $\chi^2(24)$ is 12.40, and the 0.975-quantile is 39.36, so the rejection region is

$$t \leq 12.40 \quad \text{and} \quad t \geq 39.36.$$

For these data,

$$k = 25, \quad \textstyle\sum x_i = 211, \quad \sum x_i^2 = 2133,$$
$$\textstyle\sum (x_i - \overline{x})^2 = 352.16,$$

so the observed value of T is

$$t = \frac{25 \times 352.16}{211} \simeq 41.73.$$

This is in the rejection region, so the null hypothesis that the spatial pattern of white oak trees is random is rejected at the 5% significance level.

Since the observed value t is larger than expected, there is evidence of clustering of the white oak trees.

Solution 13.2

For Figure 13.3, $M = 53$ and $k = 37$, so M/k, the average number of objects per quadrat, is less than 4. Hence it is not appropriate to apply the χ^2 dispersion test.

It would be possible to apply the test if the quadrats were combined into larger areas.

Solution 13.3

Although the quadrats are different shapes, they all have the same area.

Also, for these data

$$k = 24,$$
$$M = \textstyle\sum x_i = 436 > 20,$$

so

$$M/k \simeq 18.17 > 4.$$

Hence the conditions for applying the χ^2 dispersion test are satisfied.

Since $k = 24$, the null distribution of T is $\chi^2(23)$. From Table 3 in the *Handbook*, the 0.005-quantile of $\chi^2(23)$ is 9.26, and the 0.995-quantile is 44.18, so the rejection region is

$$t \leq 9.26 \quad \text{and} \quad t \geq 44.18.$$

For these data,

$$\textstyle\sum x_i^2 = 11\,008, \quad \sum (x_i - \overline{x})^2 = 3087.33\ldots\,.$$

Therefore the observed value of T is

$$t = \frac{24 \times 3087.33\ldots}{436} \simeq 169.94.$$

This is in the rejection region, so the null hypothesis that the woodlice are distributed randomly in the beech litter is rejected at the 1% significance level.

Since the observed value is larger than expected, there is evidence of clustering of the woodlice.

Solution 13.4

To use square quadrats would involve waste of information along the diagonal. The area of survey of region I is a right-angled triangle, so it can conveniently be divided into quadrats of the same shape. The number of quadrats k must be chosen so that $M/k \geq 4$. Since $M = 72$, k must be not greater than 18. A convenient number of quadrats would be 16.

Solution 13.5

The effective area served by the post offices – that is, the total area in the rectangular frame less the area of parks and river – needs to be divided into quadrats of equal area. These can be of irregular shape, and could be constructed by counting squares on graph paper, for instance. There may be some loss of coverage at the boundaries of the parks and river, but this needs to be kept to a minimum. The procedure is rather messy and time-consuming, but nonetheless practicable.

Solution 13.6

Since $n = 5$, the null distribution of the test statistic H is $F(10, 10)$.

The 0.005-quantile of $F(10, 10)$ is 0.171, and the 0.995-quantile is 5.847, so the rejection region of the test is

$$h \leq 0.171 \quad \text{and} \quad h \geq 5.847.$$

The observed value of H is

$$h = \frac{\sum r_i^2}{\sum s_i^2} = \frac{527}{51} \simeq 10.33.$$

This is in the rejection region, so the null hypothesis that the redwood seedlings are randomly distributed in region II can be rejected at the 1% significance level.

Since the observed value $h = 10.33$ is considerably greater than 1, there is evidence that the seedlings are clustered in the region.

Solution 13.7

(a) From the solution to Activity 13.1, the null distribution of the test statistic T is $\chi^2(24)$, and the observed value t of T is 41.73. The 0.975-quantile of $\chi^2(24)$ is 39.36, and the 0.99-quantile is 42.98, so

$$0.01 < P(T \geq 41.73) < 0.025.$$

The test is two-sided, so $0.02 < p < 0.05$.

Hence there is moderate evidence against the null hypothesis of randomness. Since the observed value t is large, there is evidence of clustering of the white oak trees.

(b) From the solution to Activity 13.6, the null distribution of the test statistic H is $F(10, 10)$, and the observed value h of H is 10.33. The 0.995-quantile of $F(10, 10)$ is 5.847, so

$$P(H \geq 10.33) < 0.005.$$

The test is two-sided, so $p < 0.01$.

Hence there is strong evidence against the null hypothesis that the redwood seedlings are randomly distributed in region II. Since the observed value h is large, there is evidence of clustering of the redwood seedlings.

Solutions to Exercises

Solution 3.1

The rate at which events occur is

$$\lambda = \tfrac{1}{16} \text{ per minute} = 3.75 \text{ per hour.}$$

(a) The waiting time between events has an exponential distribution with parameter $\lambda = 3.75$.

(b) The number of events in any hour-long interval, $N(1)$, has a Poisson distribution with mean 3.75.

(c) The time intervals 2 pm–3 pm and 3 pm–4 pm are disjoint, so what happened between 2 pm and 3 pm does not influence what happens in the next hour. The probability of at most one event between 3 pm and 4 pm is

$$P(N(1) \leq 1) = e^{-3.75}(1 + 3.75) \simeq 0.1117.$$

(d) The probability required is

$$\begin{aligned} P(T > 0.5) = 1 - F(0.5) &= e^{-3.75\times 0.5} \\ &= e^{-1.875} \\ &\simeq 0.1534. \end{aligned}$$

Solution 3.2

The eruption rate is

$$\lambda = 1 \text{ per 29 months} = \tfrac{1}{29} \text{ per month.}$$

(a) The number of eruptions during a five-year period, $N(60)$, has a Poisson distribution with parameter

$$\lambda t = \left(\tfrac{1}{29} \text{ per month}\right) \times (60 \text{ months}) \simeq 2.069,$$

so the expected number of eruptions is 2.069.

(b) The probability of exactly two eruptions is

$$P(N(60) = 2) = \frac{e^{-2.069}(2.069)^2}{2!} \simeq 0.2704.$$

(c) By the memoryless property of the exponential distribution, the time between the start of observation and any previous event can be ignored. If T is the time from the start of observation until the next eruption then, since $P(T \geq t) = e^{-\lambda t}$, where t is in months,

$$P(T \geq 36) = e^{-36/29} \simeq 0.2890.$$

Solution 3.3

(a) The mean time between events is 3 months, so each random number e_n from Table 6 in the *Handbook* must be multiplied by 3 to give a simulated time between events in months. The realisation is shown in Table S.4.

Table S.4

n	e_n	$3e_n$	$w_n = t_1 + \cdots + t_n$
1	3.5677	10.7031	$10.7031 \simeq 10.70$
2	4.1622	12.4866	$23.1897 \simeq 23.19$
3	0.6071	1.8213	$25.0110 \simeq 25.01$

(b) From Table S.4, it is evident that the third event occurred outside the 24-month period being modelled. So two failures were observed: the first occurring after 10.70 months, the second after 23.19 months. The number 2 is a single observation from the Poisson distribution with parameter $24/3 = 8$.

Solution 5.1

The rate at which customers arrive is $\lambda = 8$ per hour. The proportions of customers in the three categories are $p_1 = 0.70$, $p_2 = 0.05$, $p_3 = 0.25$, where the categories are letters, parcels and non-postal, respectively.

(a) The parcel rate is

$$\lambda_2 = \lambda p_2 = 8 \times 0.05 = 0.4 \text{ per hour.}$$

(b) The time T between arrivals of customers posting parcels has an exponential distribution with parameter λ_2, so the probability that the interval between the arrivals of such customers is greater than an hour is

$$P(T > 1) = e^{-\lambda_2 \times 1} = e^{-0.4} \simeq 0.6703.$$

(c) The letter rate is

$$\lambda_1 = \lambda p_1 = 8 \times 0.70 = 5.6 \text{ per hour.}$$

Let $L(t)$ be the number of customers arriving to post letters in t hours. Then $L(3)$, the number of customers posting letters in a three-hour period, has a Poisson distribution with parameter

$$\lambda_1 t = 5.6 \text{ per hour} \times 3 \text{ hours} = 16.8.$$

The probability that there are fewer than five such customers is

$$\begin{aligned} &P(L(3) \leq 4) \\ &= e^{-16.8}\left(1 + 16.8 + \frac{16.8^2}{2!} + \frac{16.8^3}{3!} + \frac{16.8^4}{4!}\right) \\ &\simeq e^{-16.8} \times 4268.33 \\ &\simeq 0.000\,22. \end{aligned}$$

(d) The arrival rate of customers posting letters or parcels is $\lambda(p_1 + p_2) = 8 \times 0.75 = 6$ per hour.

The waiting time between arrivals of such customers is $M(6)$, so the median waiting time (in hours) is the solution of the equation

$$F(t) = 1 - e^{-6t} = \tfrac{1}{2},$$

that is,

$$e^{-6t} = \tfrac{1}{2}.$$

Therefore the median waiting time is

$$\begin{aligned} t &= \tfrac{1}{6} \log 2 \text{ hours} \\ &= 10 \times \log 2 \text{ minutes} \\ &\simeq 6.93 \text{ minutes.} \end{aligned}$$

Solution 5.2

The arrival rates of works of fiction, biographies, works of reference and non-text items are $\lambda_1 = 8$ per week, $\lambda_2 = 1$ per week, $\lambda_3 = 0.25$ per week, $\lambda_4 = 5$ per week, respectively.

(a) Let $N(1)$ be the number of non-text items that arrive in one week; then $N(1) \sim \text{Poisson}(5)$. So the probability that at least two non-text acquisitions will arrive next week is given by

$$\begin{aligned} P(N(1) \geq 2) &= 1 - P(N(1) \leq 1) \\ &= 1 - e^{-5}(1+5) \\ &\simeq 0.9596. \end{aligned}$$

(b) Let $W(t)$ be the number of works of fiction that arrive in t weeks, so the number that arrive in one day is $W(\frac{1}{7})$. Since $\lambda_1 = 8$ per week, $W(\frac{1}{7}) \sim \text{Poisson}(\frac{8}{7})$. The probability that no new work of fiction will arrive tomorrow is

$$P(W(\tfrac{1}{7}) = 0) = e^{-8/7} \simeq 0.3189.$$

(c) The proportions of new acquisitions in each of the four categories are

$$\begin{aligned} p_{\text{fiction}} &= \frac{\lambda_1}{\lambda_1+\lambda_2+\lambda_3+\lambda_4} \\ &= \frac{8}{8+1+0.25+5} \\ &= \frac{8}{14.25} \simeq 0.561, \end{aligned}$$

$$p_{\text{biography}} = \frac{1}{14.25} \simeq 0.070,$$

$$p_{\text{reference}} = \frac{0.25}{14.25} \simeq 0.018,$$

$$p_{\text{non-text}} = \frac{5}{14.25} \simeq 0.351.$$

Solution 6.1

(a) A sketch of the function $\lambda(t)$ for $0 \leq t \leq 4$ is shown in Figure S.5.

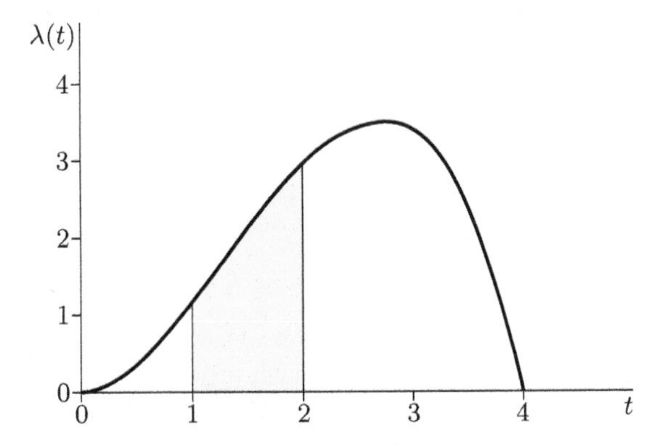

Figure S.5 The event rate $\lambda(t) = \frac{3}{8}t^2(4-t)$, $0 \leq t \leq 4$

The shaded area represents the expected number of events between $t = 1$ and $t = 2$.

(b) The expected number of events that occur by time t is

$$\begin{aligned} \mu(t) = \int_0^t \lambda(u)\,du &= \int_0^t \tfrac{3}{8}u^2(4-u)\,du \\ &= \tfrac{3}{8}\int_0^t (4u^2 - u^3)\,du \\ &= \tfrac{3}{8}\left[\tfrac{4}{3}u^3 - \tfrac{1}{4}u^4\right]_0^t \\ &= \tfrac{1}{2}t^3 - \tfrac{3}{32}t^4. \end{aligned}$$

(c) The expected number of events between $t = 1$ and $t = 3$ is

$$\begin{aligned} \mu(1,3) &= \mu(3) - \mu(1) \\ &= \left(\tfrac{1}{2}\times 3^3 - \tfrac{3}{32}\times 3^4\right) - \left(\tfrac{1}{2}\times 1^3 - \tfrac{3}{32}\times 1^4\right) \\ &= 5.906\,25 - 0.406\,25 \\ &= 5.5. \end{aligned}$$

The expected total number of events is

$$\mu(4) = \tfrac{1}{2}\times 4^3 - \tfrac{3}{32}\times 4^4 = 8.$$

(d) The number of events between $t = 1$ and $t = 3$, $X(1,3)$, has a Poisson distribution with parameter 5.5. The probability of more than two events between $t = 1$ and $t = 3$ is given by

$$\begin{aligned} P(X(1,3) > 2) &= 1 - P(X(1,3) \leq 2) \\ &= 1 - e^{-5.5}\left(1 + 5.5 + \frac{5.5^2}{2!}\right) \\ &= 1 - e^{-5.5}(21.625) \\ &\simeq 1 - 0.0884 \\ &= 0.9116. \end{aligned}$$

(e) Given that (exactly) two events occur between $t = 0$ and $t = 1$, the probability that at least four events occur in total is just the probability that at least two events occur between $t = 1$ and $t = 4$, that is,

$$P(X(1,4) \geq 2).$$

The number of events, $X(1,4)$, has a Poisson distribution with parameter

$$\mu(1,4) = \mu(4) - \mu(1) = 8 - 0.406\,25 = 7.593\,75.$$

Therefore

$$\begin{aligned} P(X(1,4) \geq 2) &= 1 - P(X(1,4) \leq 1) \\ &= 1 - e^{-7.593\,75}(1 + 7.593\,75) \\ &\simeq 0.9957. \end{aligned}$$

Solution 6.2

The event rate is $\lambda(t) = 3t^2$, so

$$\mu(t) = \int_0^t \lambda(u)\,du = \int_0^t 3u^2\,du = t^3.$$

The simulated times may be found using (6.8):

$$\mu(w_{j+1}) = \mu(w_j) - \log(1-u).$$

In this case,

$$w_{j+1}^3 = w_j^3 - \log(1-u),$$

so

$$w_{j+1} = \sqrt[3]{w_j^3 - \log(1-u)}.$$

The simulated times are

$$w_1 = \sqrt[3]{w_0^3 - \log(1-u_1)}$$
$$= \sqrt[3]{-\log(1-0.240\,36)} \simeq 0.650\,23 \simeq 0.650,$$
$$w_2 = \sqrt[3]{0.650\,23^3 - \log(1-0.290\,38)}$$
$$\simeq 0.851\,76 \simeq 0.852,$$
$$w_3 = \sqrt[3]{0.851\,76^3 - \log(1-0.432\,11)} \simeq 1.057\,85 > 1.$$

The simulation is required only for $0 \leq t \leq 1$, so two events occur, at $t_1 = 0.650$ and $t_2 = 0.852$.

Solution 7.1

(a) The mean of Y is given by

$$\mu = E(Y) = 0 \times 0.03 + 1 \times 0.84 + 2 \times 0.12 + 3 \times 0.01$$
$$= 0 + 0.84 + 0.24 + 0.03$$
$$= 1.11.$$

Similarly,

$$E(Y^2) = 0 \times 0.03 + 1 \times 0.84 + 4 \times 0.12 + 9 \times 0.01$$
$$= 0 + 0.84 + 0.48 + 0.09$$
$$= 1.41.$$

So the variance of Y is given by

$$\sigma^2 = V(Y) = E(Y^2) - (E(Y))^2$$
$$= 1.41 - 1.11^2$$
$$= 0.1779.$$

(b) The arrival rate of letters is $\lambda = 18$ per day, and the length of the period is $t = 20$ days. So, using (7.5) and (7.6), the mean and variance of the total number of complaints received are given by

$$E[S(20)] = 1.11 \times 18 \times 20 = 399.6,$$
$$V[S(20)] = 18 \times 20 \times (0.1779 + 1.11^2) = 507.6.$$

Solution 7.2

The mean and variance of the number of tasks per vehicle are $\mu = 0.8$ and $\sigma^2 = 0.8$.

The rate at which cars are returned is $\lambda = 60$ per week, and the length of time is $t = 4$ weeks. So the mean and variance of the total number of unscheduled tasks required of the maintenance staff are given by

$$E[S(4)] = 0.8 \times 60 \times 4 = 192,$$
$$V[S(4)] = 60 \times 4 \times (0.8 + 0.8^2) = 345.6.$$

Solution 8.1

From part (a) of the solution to Exercise 7.1, $\mu = E(Y) = 1.11$ and $\sigma^2 = V(Y) = 0.1779$.

Using Formula (8.1),

$$I(t) = \frac{\sigma^2}{\mu} + \mu = \frac{0.1779}{1.11} + 1.11 \simeq 1.27.$$

Since $I(t) > 1$, arrivals of complaints are more variable than they would be if complaints arrived according to a Poisson process.

Solution 8.2

From the solution to Exercise 7.2, $\mu = 0.8$ and $\sigma^2 = 0.8$, so using (8.1),

$$I(t) = \frac{\sigma^2}{\mu} + \mu = \frac{0.8}{0.8} + 0.8 = 1.8.$$

Since $I(t) > 1$, occurrences of unscheduled maintenance tasks are more variable than they would be if they occurred according to a Poisson process.

Solution 10.1

Let N be the number of objects in a square region with sides 30 cm long. Then N has a Poisson distribution with parameter

$$\lambda A = 20 \times 0.3 \times 0.3 = 1.8.$$

Hence

$$P(N = 3) = \frac{e^{-1.8} 1.8^3}{3!} \simeq 0.1607.$$

Solution 10.2

The number of objects in the region, N, has a Poisson distribution with parameter

$$\lambda A = 2.4 \times 10^{-3} \times 20 \times 30 = 1.44.$$

The probability required is

$$P(N > 2) = 1 - P(N \leq 2)$$
$$= 1 - e^{-1.44}\left(1 + 1.44 + \frac{1.44^2}{2!}\right)$$
$$\simeq 0.1762.$$

Solution 10.3

(a) N, the number of objects in a cordoned region, has a Poisson distribution with parameter

$$\lambda A = 2.5 \times 10^{-4} \times 100 \times 80 = 2.$$

(b) Values of the p.m.f. and c.d.f. of N are given in Table S.5.

Table S.5 Values of the p.m.f. and c.d.f.

n	0	1	2	3	...
$p(n)$	0.1353	0.2707	0.2707	0.1804	...
$F(n)$	0.1353	0.4060	0.6767	0.8571	...

The given random number is $u = 0.6831$, so

$$F(2) < u \leq F(3),$$

and hence the simulated value of N is $n = 3$.

(c) Altogether six independent observations from $U(0,1)$ are required, two for each object. One of each pair is multiplied by 100 and the other by 80 to give the coordinates of an object relative to one corner of the cordoned region:

$$x = 100u_1, \quad y = 80u_2.$$

Solution 12.1

The point-to-nearest-object distance R and the object-to-nearest-object distance S (measured in metres) both have a Rayleigh distribution with parameter $\lambda = 0.2$ per square metre and c.d.f.

$$F(x) = 1 - e^{-\pi\lambda x^2}, \quad x > 0.$$

(a) Using (12.4), the mean point-to-nearest-object distance in metres is

$$E(R) = \frac{0.5}{\sqrt{\lambda}} = \frac{0.5}{\sqrt{0.2}} \simeq 1.12.$$

Using the c.d.f. of R,

$$P(R > 2) = 1 - F(2) = e^{-\pi\times 0.2\times 2^2} = e^{-0.8\pi} \simeq 0.081.$$

(b) The mean of S (in m) is

$$E(S) = \frac{0.5}{\sqrt{\lambda}} \simeq 1.12.$$

The variance of S (in m^2) is given by

$$V(S) = \frac{4-\pi}{4\pi\lambda} = \frac{4-\pi}{0.8\pi} \simeq 0.342.$$

Using the c.d.f. of S,

$$P(S < 1) = 1 - e^{-0.2\pi} \simeq 0.467.$$

Solution 13.1

The data are in the form of counts, the sample size is $M = 144 > 20$, and the average number of objects per quadrat is $M/k = 144/30 > 4$, so the χ^2 dispersion test can be used.

The null distribution of T is $\chi^2(29)$. Using a 5% significance level, the rejection region of the test is

$$t \le 16.05 \quad \text{and} \quad t \ge 45.72.$$

Since

$$\sum x_i^2 = 7^2 + 7^2 + \cdots + 8^2 = 846,$$
$$\sum (x_i - \overline{x})^2 = 846 - 144^2/30 = 154.8,$$

the observed value of the test statistic T is

$$t = \frac{30 \times 154.8}{144} = 32.25.$$

The observed value t of T is not in the rejection region, so there is insufficient evidence to reject the hypothesis that the plants are randomly distributed over the rectangle at the 5% significance level.

Solution 13.2

(a) The appropriate test is Hopkins' test.

The null distribution of H is $F(16,16)$. Using a 5% significance level, the rejection region is

$$h \le 0.362 \quad \text{and} \quad h \ge 2.761.$$

The observed value of the test statistic H is

$$h = \frac{\sum r_i^2}{\sum s_i^2} = \frac{2.7026}{8.9320} \simeq 0.303.$$

The observed value is in the rejection region, so the null hypothesis of randomness can be rejected at the 5% significance level. Since $h < 1$, there is evidence of regularity in the pattern.

(b) If a 1% significance level is used, the rejection region is

$$h \le 0.258 \quad \text{and} \quad h \ge 3.875.$$

Since the observed value of H is not in the rejection region, there is insufficient evidence to reject the null hypothesis that the objects are randomly located at the 1% significance level.

(c) The observed value of H, which is 0.303, lies between the 0.01-quantile and the 0.025-quantile of $F(16,16)$. Since the test is two-sided, the p value for the test is between 0.02 and 0.05; that is, $0.02 < p < 0.05$. Therefore there is moderate evidence against the null hypothesis that the objects are randomly located. Since $h < 1$, the test suggests that there is regularity in the pattern.

Solution 14.1

This exercise covers some of the ideas and techniques discussed in Sections 1 and 3.

(a) Possible random processes include the following.

$\{X(t); t \ge 0\}$, where $X(t)$ is the number of failures that have occurred by time t. The state space is discrete and the time domain is continuous.

$\{T_n; n = 1, 2, \ldots\}$, where T_n is the time between the $(n-1)$th and nth failures. The state space is continuous and the time domain is discrete.

$\{W_n; n = 1, 2, \ldots\}$, where W_n is the time at which the nth failure occurs. The state space is continuous and the time domain is discrete.

There are other possibilities.

(b) Working in years, T, the interval between successive failures, has an exponential distribution with parameter $\lambda = 1.2$ per year.

Therefore

$$P(T > 1) = e^{-1.2} \simeq 0.3012.$$

(c) The number of failures in a two-year period, $N(2)$, has a Poisson distribution with parameter

$$\lambda t = (1.2 \text{ per year}) \times (2 \text{ years}) = 2.4.$$

The probability required is

$$P(N(2) = 3) = \frac{e^{-2.4} 2.4^3}{3!} \simeq 0.2090.$$

Solution 14.2

This exercise covers some of the ideas and techniques discussed in Section 3.

The rate of the Poisson process is $\lambda = 2.4$ per day $= 0.1$ per hour.

(a) The mean number of events per week is

$$\lambda t = 2.4 \text{ per day} \times 7 \text{ days} = 16.8.$$

(b) The time between events has an exponential distribution with parameter λ and mean

$$\frac{1}{\lambda} = \frac{1}{0.1 \text{ per hour}} = 10 \text{ hours}.$$

Working in days, the mean time between events is

$$\frac{1}{\lambda} = \frac{1}{2.4 \text{ per day}} = \tfrac{5}{12} \text{ day}.$$

(c) Working in days, $N(1)$, the number of events in a day, has a Poisson distribution with parameter 2.4. The probability that no event will occur on Monday next week is

$$P(N(1) = 0) = e^{-2.4} \simeq 0.0907.$$

(d) The probability that at least two events will occur on Tuesday next week is

$$\begin{aligned} P(N(1) \geq 2) &= 1 - P(N(1) \leq 1) \\ &= 1 - e^{-2.4}(1 + 2.4) \\ &\simeq 0.6916. \end{aligned}$$

Solution 14.3

This exercise covers some of the ideas and techniques discussed in Section 5.

(a) The rates at which cars, commercial vehicles and motorcycles arrive are $\lambda_1 = 12$ per hour, $\lambda_2 = 6$ per hour and $\lambda_3 = 4$ per hour, respectively.

Each type of vehicle arrives according to a Poisson process, so altogether vehicles arrive according to a Poisson process with rate

$$\lambda = \lambda_1 + \lambda_2 + \lambda_3 = 22 \text{ per hour}.$$

The number of vehicles that arrive in t hours has a Poisson distribution with parameter $22t$; that is, $N(t) \sim \text{Poisson}(22t)$.

Therefore $N\left(\frac{1}{12}\right)$, the number of vehicles that arrive in 5 minutes ($= \frac{1}{12}$ hour) has a Poisson distribution with parameter $22 \times \frac{1}{12}$, and

$$P\left(N\left(\tfrac{1}{12}\right) = 0\right) = e^{-22/12} \simeq 0.1599.$$

(b) Motorcycles arrive at the rate $\lambda_3 = 4$ per hour, so $N_{\text{M}}(1)$, the number of motorcycles that arrive in an hour, has a Poisson distribution with parameter $\lambda_3 t = 4$. The probability required is

$$P(N_{\text{M}}(1) = 4) = \frac{e^{-4}4^4}{4!} \simeq 0.1954.$$

(c) Since $\lambda = 22$ per hour, T, the time between the arrivals of successive vehicles, has an exponential distribution with parameter 22. That is, $T \sim M(22)$.

(d) Let $Y(t)$ be the total number of cars and commercial vehicles that arrive in t hours. Cars and commercial vehicles arrive at the rate $\lambda_1 + \lambda_2 = 18$ per hour, so $Y\left(\frac{1}{6}\right)$, the number of such vehicles that arrive in 10 minutes $\left(\frac{1}{6}\text{ hour}\right)$ hour, has a Poisson distribution with parameter $18 \times \frac{1}{6} = 3$. Hence the required probability is

$$\begin{aligned} P\left(Y\left(\tfrac{1}{6}\right) \geq 3\right) &= 1 - P\left(Y\left(\tfrac{1}{6}\right) \leq 2\right) \\ &= 1 - e^{-3}\left(1 + 3 + \frac{3^2}{2!}\right) \\ &\simeq 0.5768. \end{aligned}$$

(e) The probability that the next vehicle that arrives will be a car is given by

$$\frac{\lambda_1}{\lambda_1 + \lambda_2 + \lambda_2} = \frac{12}{22} \simeq 0.5455.$$

Solution 14.4

This exercise covers some of the ideas and techniques discussed in Section 6.

(a) The expected number of events in $(0, t]$ is

$$\mu(t) = \int_0^t \lambda(u)\, du = \int_0^t 30t^2\, dt = 10t^3.$$

Hence the number of events in $(0, 0.5]$ has a Poisson distribution with parameter

$$\mu(0.5) = 10 \times 0.5^3 = 1.25.$$

The probability required is

$$\begin{aligned} P(X(0.5) < 3) &= e^{-1.25}\left(1 + 1.25 + \frac{1.25^2}{2}\right) \\ &\simeq 0.868. \end{aligned}$$

(b) The number of events in the interval $(0.5, 0.6]$ has a Poisson distribution with parameter

$$\begin{aligned} \mu(0.5, 0.6) &= \mu(0.6) - \mu(0.5) \\ &= 10 \times 0.6^3 - 10 \times 0.5^3 \\ &= 0.91. \end{aligned}$$

Therefore

$$P(X(0.5, 0.6) \leq 1) = e^{-0.91}(1 + 0.91) \simeq 0.769.$$

(c) The probability required is

$$\begin{aligned} &P(X(0.5, 1) = 5 \mid X(0, 1) = 5) \\ &= \frac{P(X(0.5, 1) = 5 \text{ and } X(0, 1) = 5)}{P(X(0, 1) = 5)} \\ &= \frac{P(X(0, 0.5) = 0 \text{ and } X(0.5, 1) = 5)}{P(X(0, 1) = 5)} \\ &= \frac{P(X(0, 0.5) = 0) \times P(X(0.5, 1) = 5)}{P(X(0, 1) = 5)}. \end{aligned}$$

Since $\mu(1) = 10$, $\mu(0.5) = 1.25$ and $\mu(0.5, 1) = \mu(1) - \mu(0.5) = 8.75$,

$$X(0, 0.5) \sim \text{Poisson}(1.25),$$
$$X(0.5, 1) \sim \text{Poisson}(8.75),$$
$$X(0, 1) \sim \text{Poisson}(10).$$

Hence the probability required is

$$e^{-1.25} \times \frac{e^{-8.75}8.75^5}{5!} \bigg/ \frac{e^{-10}10^5}{5!} \simeq 0.513.$$

Solution 14.5

This exercise covers some of the ideas and techniques discussed in Section 6.

(a) The graph of $\lambda(t)$ is shown in Figure S.6.

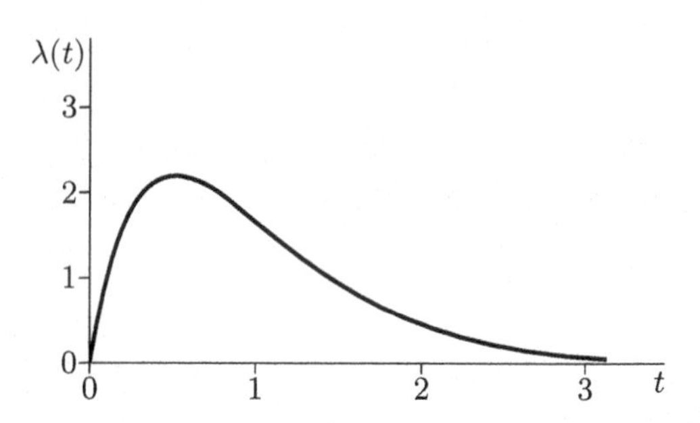

Figure S.6 The rate $\lambda(t) = 12te^{-2t}$

The rate of occurrence of events is

$$\lambda(t) = 12te^{-2t},$$

so

$$\lambda'(t) = 12e^{-2t} - 24te^{-2t}$$
$$= 0 \quad \text{when } 2t = 1.$$

The maximum occurs when $t = 0.5$.

The maximum rate is $\lambda(0.5) \simeq 2.207$ events per unit of time.

(b) The expected number of events by time t is

$$\mu(t) = \int_0^t 12ue^{-2u}\,du = 3 - e^{-2t}(3 + 6t)$$

(using integration by parts), so

$$\mu(1) \simeq 1.782.$$

Hence $X(1)$, the number of events that occur by time $t = 1$, has a Poisson distribution with parameter 1.782, and

$$P(X(1) < 3) = e^{-1.782}(1 + 1.782 + 1.782^2/2)$$
$$\simeq 0.735.$$

(c) The number of events between $t = 1$ and $t = 2$ has a Poisson distribution with parameter

$$\mu(1,2) = \mu(2) - \mu(1)$$
$$= 9e^{-2} - 15e^{-4}$$
$$\simeq 0.943.$$

Therefore

$$P(X(1,2) = 1) = 0.943e^{-0.943} \simeq 0.367.$$

(d) The number of events expected in $(0, t]$ is

$$\mu(t) = 3 - (3 + 6t)e^{-2t}.$$

The total number of events expected is $\lim_{t\to\infty} \mu(t) = 3$.

Solution 14.6

This exercise covers some of the ideas and techniques discussed in Sections 7 and 8.

(a) The mean and variance of a discrete uniform distribution with $n = 4$ are 2.5 and 1.25, respectively.

(b) For this compound Poisson process, $\mu = 2.5$ and $\sigma^2 = 1.25$, so using (7.5) and (7.6), the mean and variance of $S(t)$, the total number of occupants of cars that pass in time t, are given by

$$E[S(t)] = \mu\lambda t = 2.5\lambda t,$$

$$V[S(t)] = \lambda t(\sigma^2 + \mu^2)$$
$$= \lambda t(1.25 + 2.5^2)$$
$$= 7.5\lambda t.$$

(c) Using (8.1), the index of dispersion is

$$I(t) = \frac{\sigma^2}{\mu} + \mu = \frac{1.25}{2.5} + 2.5 = 3.$$

Since $I(t) > 1$, the pattern of car occupants passing the point is more variable than it would be if occupants passed the point according to a Poisson process.

Solution 14.7

This exercise covers some of the ideas and techniques discussed in Section 10.

(a) N, the number of objects in a cordoned region, has a Poisson distribution with parameter

$$\lambda A = 8 \times 10^{-4} \times 50 \times 40 = 1.6.$$

(b) The probability required is

$$P(N > 3) = 1 - P(N \leq 3)$$
$$= 1 - e^{-1.6}\left(1 + 1.6 + \frac{1.6^2}{2!} + \frac{1.6^3}{3!}\right)$$
$$\simeq 1 - 0.9212$$
$$= 0.0788.$$

(c) Values of the p.m.f. and c.d.f. of $N \sim \text{Poisson}(1.6)$ are given in Table S.6.

Table S.6 Values of the p.m.f. and c.d.f. of N

n	0	1	2	3	4	...
$p(n)$	0.2019	0.3230	0.2584	0.1378	0.0551	...
$F(n)$	0.2019	0.5249	0.7833	0.9211	0.9762	...

Given the random number $u = 0.9634$, the simulated value of N is $n = 4$ (since $F(3) < 0.9634 < F(4)$).

(d) Altogether eight independent observations from $U(0,1)$ are required, two for each object. One of each pair is multiplied by 50 and the other by 40 to give the coordinates of an object relative to one corner of the cordoned region:

$$x = 50u_1, \quad y = 40u_2.$$

Solution 14.8

This exercise covers some of the ideas and techniques discussed in Section 12.

The point-to-nearest-object distance R and the object-to-nearest-object distance S both have a Rayleigh distribution with parameter $\lambda = 8 \times 10^{-4}$ and c.d.f.

$$F(x) = 1 - e^{-\pi\lambda x^2}, \quad x > 0,$$

where x is in metres.

(a) Using (12.4), the mean object-to-nearest-object distance in metres is

$$E(S) = \frac{0.5}{\sqrt{\lambda}} = \frac{0.5}{\sqrt{8 \times 10^{-4}}} \simeq 17.7.$$

Using the c.d.f. of S,

$$P(S < 10) = 1 - e^{-0.08\pi} \simeq 0.222.$$

(b) Using the c.d.f. of R,

$$P(R > 30) = e^{-0.72\pi} \simeq 0.104.$$

Solution 14.9

This exercise covers some of the ideas and techniques discussed in Section 13.

(a) The data are in the form of counts, and $M = 180 > 20$ and $M/k = 180/40 > 4$, so the χ^2 dispersion test can be used.

The null distribution of T is $\chi^2(39)$.

Using a 5% significance level, the rejection region is

$$t \leq 23.65 \quad \text{and} \quad t \geq 58.12.$$

The observed value of T is

$$t = \frac{40 \times 274}{180} \simeq 60.89.$$

The observed value of T is in the rejection region, so the hypothesis of randomness is rejected at the 5% significance level. Since the observed value of T is greater than 58.12, there is evidence of clustering of the wild flowers in the wood.

(b) The observed value of T is 60.89. This lies between the 0.975-quantile and the 0.99-quantile of $\chi^2(39)$. Since the test is two-sided, it follows that $0.02 < p < 0.05$. Therefore the test provides moderate evidence against the null hypothesis that the wild flowers are distributed randomly in the wood. Since the observed value is large, the test suggests that there is clustering of the flowers.

Solution 14.10

This exercise covers some of the ideas and techniques discussed in Section 13.

When the data are in the form of distances, Hopkins' test is appropriate.

The null distribution of the test statistic H is $F(40, 40)$. For a 5% significance level, the rejection region is

$$h \leq 0.533 \quad \text{and} \quad h \geq 1.875.$$

The observed value of H is

$$h = \frac{\sum r_i^2}{\sum s_i^2} = \frac{0.10^2 + \cdots + 0.16^2}{0.20^2 + \cdots + 0.33^2} = \frac{1.3294}{1.9932} \simeq 0.6670.$$

The observed value h of H is not in the rejection region, so there is insufficient evidence to reject the hypothesis that the plants are randomly located in the rectangle at the 5% significance level.

Solution 14.11

This exercise covers some of the ideas and techniques discussed in Section 3.

(a) The random variable W_3 is the sum of three independent exponential random variables, so it has the gamma distribution $\Gamma(3, \lambda)$. Working in hours, $\lambda = 0.1$ per hour, so $W_3 \sim \Gamma(3, 0.1)$. From Table 9 in the *Handbook*, the p.d.f. of W_3 is

$$f(w) = \frac{e^{-0.1w} w^{3-1} (0.1)^3}{(3-1)!} = 0.0005w^2 e^{-w/10}, \quad 0 \leq w < \infty.$$

(b) The c.d.f. of W_3 is given by

$$F(w) = \int_0^w f(x)\, dx = \int_0^w 0.0005x^2 e^{-x/10}\, dx.$$

Integration by parts must be used twice:

$$\begin{aligned}
F(w) &= \int_0^w 0.0005x^2 e^{-x/10}\, dx \\
&= \left[0.0005x^2\left(-10e^{-x/10}\right)\right]_0^w + \int_0^w 10e^{-x/10}(0.001x)\, dx \\
&= -0.005w^2 e^{-w/10} + \int_0^w 0.01xe^{-x/10}\, dx \\
&= -0.005w^2 e^{-w/10} + \left[0.01x\left(-10e^{-x/10}\right)\right]_0^w + \int_0^w 10e^{-x/10}(0.01)\, dx \\
&= -0.005w^2 e^{-w/10} - 0.1we^{-w/10} + \int_0^w 0.1e^{-x/10}\, dx \\
&= -0.005w^2 e^{-w/10} - 0.1we^{-w/10} + 1 - e^{-w/10} \\
&= 1 - e^{-w/10}\left(1 + 0.1w + 0.005w^2\right).
\end{aligned}$$

Therefore

$$\begin{aligned}
P(W_3 > 30) &= 1 - F(30) \\
&= e^{-30/10}\left(1 + 0.1 \times 30 + 0.005 \times 30^2\right) \\
&= 8.5e^{-3} \\
&\simeq 0.4232.
\end{aligned}$$

Solution 14.12

This exercise covers some of the ideas and techniques discussed in Section 5.

(a) Since the Poisson processes are independent and each has rate λ, the rate of the multivariate Poisson process obtained by superposing the events in the processes on the same time axis is

$$\lambda + \lambda + \cdots + \lambda = n\lambda.$$

Hence U_1 has an exponential distribution with parameter $n\lambda$: $U_1 \sim M(n\lambda)$.

(b) The waiting time U_2 will be less than or equal to u if at least one event occurs in each process by time u.

For each process,

$$P(T \leq u) = 1 - e^{-\lambda u}.$$

Therefore

$$P(U_2 \leq u) = (P(T \leq u))^n = (1 - e^{-\lambda u})^n.$$

This is the c.d.f. of U_2.

(c) When $n = 2$, the c.d.f. of U_2 is $F(u) = (1 - e^{-\lambda u})^2$. So, using the alternative formula for the mean,

$$\begin{aligned} E(U_2) &= \int_0^\infty (1 - F(u))\,du \\ &= \int_0^\infty (2e^{-\lambda u} - e^{-2\lambda u})\,du \\ &= \left[-\frac{2}{\lambda}e^{-\lambda u} + \frac{1}{2\lambda}e^{-2\lambda u}\right]_0^\infty \\ &= \frac{2}{\lambda} - \frac{1}{2\lambda} \\ &= \frac{3}{2\lambda}. \end{aligned}$$

Solution 14.13

This exercise covers some of the ideas and techniques discussed in Section 7.

Formulas (7.5) and (7.6) were derived for the situation where the random variable Y has a discrete distribution. In fact, these formulas also hold when Y has a continuous distribution. (The derivation is similar in this case.)

The mean and variance of Y, the size of a claim (in pounds), where $Y \sim \Gamma(2, 0.016)$, are

$$\mu = E(Y) = \frac{2}{0.016} = 125,$$

$$\sigma^2 = V(Y) = \frac{2}{0.016^2} = 7812.5.$$

Using (7.5) and (7.6) with $\lambda = 3$ per day and $t = 30$ days, the mean and variance of $S(30)$, the total amount claimed (in pounds) in 30 days, are

$$E[S(30)] = \mu\lambda t = 125 \times 3 \times 30 = 11\,250,$$

$$\begin{aligned} V[S(30)] &= \lambda t(\sigma^2 + \mu^2) \\ &= 3 \times 30 \times (7812.5 + 125^2) \\ &= 2\,109\,375. \end{aligned}$$

Solution 14.14

This exercise covers some of the ideas and techniques discussed in Section 12.

For a one-dimensional Poisson process in space, the event $S > s$ occurs if there is no object for a distance s on either side of the chosen object. Therefore

$$P(S > s) = e^{-\lambda s} \times e^{-\lambda s} = e^{-2\lambda s},$$

and hence the c.d.f. of S is given by

$$F(s) = 1 - P(S > s) = 1 - e^{-2\lambda s}.$$

This is the c.d.f. of an exponential distribution with parameter 2λ, so $S \sim M(2\lambda)$. Therefore $E(S) = 1/(2\lambda)$.

The distribution of R is the same as the distribution of S, so $R \sim M(2\lambda)$.

Solution 14.15

This exercise covers some of the ideas and techniques discussed in Section 12.

(a) Let $X = R^2$. Then

$$\begin{aligned} F(x) &= P(X \le x) \\ &= P(R^2 \le x) \\ &= P(R \le \sqrt{x}), \quad \text{since } R \ge 0, \\ &= 1 - e^{-\pi\lambda x}. \end{aligned}$$

Hence R^2 has an exponential distribution with parameter $\pi\lambda$.

(b) Let $Y = R_1^2 + R_2^2 + \cdots + R_n^2$.

From part (a), $R_i^2 = X_i \sim M(\pi\lambda)$ for each i.

Since the X_i are independent variates and $Y = X_1 + X_2 + \cdots + X_n$, it follows that Y has the gamma distribution $\Gamma(n, \pi\lambda)$.

Solution 14.16

This exercise covers some of the ideas and techniques discussed in Section 12.

(a) The c.d.f. of R is given by

$$F(r) = P(R \le r) = 1 - P(R > r).$$

Now, $P(R > r)$ is the probability that there is no object inside a sphere of radius r, that is, within a sphere of volume $\frac{4}{3}\pi r^3$.

The number of objects in a volume V has a Poisson distribution with parameter λV, so the number of objects in a volume $\frac{4}{3}\pi r^3$ is Poisson$(4\lambda\pi r^3/3)$.

Therefore

$$P(R > r) = e^{-4\lambda\pi r^3/3},$$

and hence the c.d.f. of R is given by

$$F(r) = 1 - e^{-4\lambda\pi r^3/3}.$$

(b) The median m satisfies $F(m) = 0.5$, that is,

$$e^{-4\lambda\pi m^3/3} = 0.5,$$

so

$$\frac{4\lambda\pi m^3}{3} = \log 2$$

or

$$m^3 = \frac{3\log 2}{4\pi\lambda} \simeq \frac{0.1655}{\lambda}.$$

Hence

$$m \simeq 0.549\lambda^{-1/3}.$$

(c) The probability that there is no planet within a million million miles is

$$P(R > r) = e^{-4\lambda\pi r^3/3},$$

where

$$\begin{aligned} r &= 10^{12}, \\ \lambda &= \frac{15}{(186\,000 \times 60 \times 60 \times 24 \times 365.2425)^3} \\ &\simeq 7.417\,666 \times 10^{-38}. \end{aligned}$$

With these values of r and λ, $4\lambda\pi r^3/3 \simeq 0.3107$, so the required probability is $e^{-0.3107} \simeq 0.733$.

Acknowledgements

Grateful acknowledgement is made to the following sources.

Figure 9.3, T.F. Cox; Figure 9.6, The Biometrika Trustees; Figure 9.7, The Royal Statistical Society; Figures 13.3 and 13.4, Blackwell Scientific Publications Ltd.

Part III is based on material written by Professor T. Lewis, who owns the copyright for the original work. Permission has been granted to rewrite the material for this book.

Index

Bernoulli process 9
  two-dimensional 60
Bernoulli trial 9

χ^2 dispersion test 81
clusters 70
compound event 44
compound Poisson process 44, 47
  index of dispersion 50
continuous-time random process 7
  notation 22, 23
count 72
counts of objects 73

density 61
discrete-time random process 7
distance 72

F distribution 85
fixed-level test 82

heterogeneity of habitat 70
hexagonal lattice 68
Hopkins' test 85

index of dispersion
  for a compound Poisson process 50
  for a point process 49
  for a spatial pattern 73
inhibition 69
inter-event time 30
interpretation of p values 88

lattice 68
lattice pattern
  with independent random displacements 68
  with random deaths 69

multivariate Poisson process 31

non-homogeneous Poisson process 34, 36
  basic results 36
  postulates 36
  simulation 40
notation for continuous-time processes 22, 23

object 58
object-to-nearest-object distance 75, 77

pattern
  with clustering 70
  with regularity 67
point process 49
point-to-nearest-object distance 75, 76
Poisson process 17, 20
  assumptions 20
  formal approach 25
  inter-event time 30
  postulates 26
  simulation 23, 62
  two main results 21
  two-dimensional 60, 61
  waiting time 21, 30
p value 87

quadrat 73, 83

random pattern 64
random process 6
  continuous-time 7
  discrete-time 7
random spatial pattern 64
randomly-positioned clusters model 71
Rayleigh distribution 76, 78
R-distance 76
realisation 6
reproductive clumping 70

S-distance 76
sequential inhibition process 69
significance testing 87
simple sequential inhibition process 69
simulation
  non-homogeneous Poisson process 40
  Poisson process 23
  two-dimensional Poisson process 64
square lattice 60, 68
state space 8
stochastic process 6

time domain 8
times of events 39
transect 55, 62
triangular lattice 68
two-dimensional Bernoulli process 60
two-dimensional Poisson process 60
  postulates 61
  simulation 64

waiting time 21